Linear Goal Programming

Linear Goal Programming

Marc J. Schniederjans

University of Nebraska

PETROCELLI BOOKS
Princeton, New Jersey

Copyright © 1984 Petrocelli Books, Inc.
All rights reserved
Printed in the United States of America
1 2 3 4 5 6 7 8 9 10

Book design by Liz Waite
Composition by Merri Typesetting

Library of Congress Cataloging in Publication Data

Schniederjans,Marc J.
    Linear goal programming.

    Bibliography: p.
    Includes index.
    1. Linear programming. I. Title.
    T57.74.S36 1984   519.7'2   84–12045
    ISBN 0-89433-243-0

Contents

Part II: Cases

To my mother and father, Florence and Oliver,
who always put their children's needs
at the highest priority.

Preface

Purpose: A special case of linear programming is linear goal programming. Linear Goal Programming (LGP) is a constrained optimization technique. It is a tool used by decision makers to solve multivariable, multigoal problems. LGP has been applied to study problems in the functional areas of accounting, finance, management and marketing. LGP has also been applied in problem solving in service industries such as health, education and the military. As global shortages of resources within business organizations and within service industries increase, the need for constrained optimization techniques that can optimally allocate those resources will continue to increase. The purpose of this book is to equip students with an understanding of how linear programming and in particular LGP can be used as an aid in constrained optimization decision making. The aim of this book is to expose students to LGP problem formulation and solution analysis procedures using both text and cases. The use of case problems is designed to reinforce the understanding of the text material and provide students with an extensive application background on the use of LGP within the functional areas of a business organization and several service industries.

Prerequisites: The level of this book is appropriate for upper-level undergraduate and graduate students in business, engineering and applied mathematics curriculums. This book is self-contained. No prior knowledge of linear programming or LGP is needed.

Approach: This book is divided into two parts: a *text section* (Part I) and a *case section* (Part II). The text section equips students on the history, formulation and solution procedures (i.e., computations and computer coding) of LGP as well as the necessary prerequisite linear programming formulation and solution procedures.

This section of the book will provide students with a greater understanding of (a) the availability of LGP models in the literature, and thus encourages students to use their libraries as a resource center, (b) how to formulate and solve linear programming problems, and (c) how to formulate and solve LGP problems by hand or with the aid of a computer. Each of the chapters in Part I are followed by a set of key vocabulary terms used within the chapter. These terms are presented as a basis for the student to review the chapter. Each chapter is followed by a set of questions, also designed to aid in chapter review.

The case section of the book exposes students to a series of LGP problem situations. Each of the cases are based in part on a "real world" consulting-type problem situation. The setting of the cases include problems in the functional areas of business (i.e., accounting, finance, management and marketing) and in the select service industries of health, education and the military. The problematic nature of the cases include LGP problem formulation, solution, and post-solution analysis. Each case is followed by several suggested article references that will aid the student in understanding the case problem. Each case is also followed by several questions. These questions are designed to guide the students' understanding of the case problem's requirements and can be used for class discussion where appropriate.

Organization: In Part I, Chapter 1 presents a brief overview of significant contributions by authors to the subject of LGP. Also presented is an extensive bibliography of articles on the subject of LGP. Each article has been identified by its application to a functional business area or service industry. Chapter 2 provides prerequisite linear programming information. Both linear programming formulation and solution procedures are presented. Chapter 3 discusses how LGP problems can be formulated. Several formulation applications are presented along with LGP modeling limitations. In Chapter 4 an LGP simplex solution procedure is described and applied. In addition, the resolution of several simplex procedural complications and problem requirements are presented. These complications include ties in pivotal rows and columns, problems requiring integer solutions and sensitivity analysis. Chapter 5 describes two computer programs for solving LGP problems on a large computer system (i.e., macro computer) and on a small computer system (i.e., micro computer) and the coding instructions for using the LGP programs.

These five text chapters are independent in the sense that any one of the chapters or combination of chapters can be excluded without affecting the use of the rest of the book. This will allow schools who have LGP computer software or prefer their own LGP solution approach to use their own resources rather than being forced to use the one presented in this text.

In Part II, a series of 11 cases are presented, comprising the remaining chapters of this book. Each of these cases are independent and may be excluded, or studied in any order. They are also independent of the LGP solution procedure presented in Chapters 4 and 5. Hence, any LGP solution procedure or computer software may be used in conjunction with the cases.

The cases can be classified by their educational exercise objective or objectives (i.e., *problem formulation:* requiring modeling of LGP problems; *problem solution:* requiring a solution for an LGP problem; *post-solution analysis:* requiring sensitivity analysis). The *problem solution* educational objective can also be divided into problems requiring integer solutions and noninteger solutions. All of the cases can also be classified by whether their analyzation requires the use of a computer or not.

The following diagram classifies the case problems in accordance to the classifications schemes mentioned above. An "x" in the diagram indicates that the case possesses a particular problem requirement.

■ Acknowledgments

This book could not have been published if it were not for the assistance of a number of individuals. I would like to thank David L. Olson of Texas A & M University who wrote the linear goal programming "Macro Computer Program" used in this book, and George Ditmore, II, of E.G.&G., Inc. of Dahlgren, Virginia, who wrote the linear goal programming "Micro Computer Program" also used in this book. I particularly appreciate the many comments and suggestions offered by N. K. Kwak (Saint Louis University), Sang M. Lee (University of Nebraska), and J. P. Ignizio (Pennsylvania State University). Administrative and secretarial support was expertly provided by Joyce Anderson, Cindy LeGrande, Joye Hearn, and especially Cathy Jensen. I am also grateful for the personal assistance of Orlando R. Petrocelli and the great help of his editorial staff.

Finally, I deeply appreciate the continuing support of my wife, Jill, and my son, Alexander (Xan).

Marc J. Schniederjans

Case Classification by Problem Requirements

Chapter No.	Area of Application	Formulation	Solution Integer	Solution Non-Integer	Post-Solution Analysis	Computer	No Computer
6	Accounting	x					x
7	Finance	x		x		x	
8	Finance	x		x		x	
9	Management	x					x
10	Management		x		x	x	
11	Management	x		x		x	
12	Management		x		x	x	
13	Marketing	x					x
14	Health			x	x	x	
15	Education	x		x		x	
16	Military	x					x

I

TEXT

■ Foreward

In addition to the chapter's general content, each chapter in Part I consists of a chapter overview *that briefly lists the chapter's subject areas, a* summary *that reviews major points discussed in the general content, a* key vocabulary *listing of terms that students should review and be familiar with, and several* chapter questions *to provide students with an immediate exercise over the general content of the chapter. Students should use these sections as aids to reinforce the learning experience of each chapter's general content.*

1

History of
Linear Goal
Programming

■ 1.1 ■ Chapter Overview

This chapter provides a brief historical introduction to the major contributions to the subject area of linear goal programming (LGP). Contained also in this chapter is an extensive bibliography of articles published using LGP. The bibliography is listed by functional areas that exist in a business and select service industries, for reference identification purposes.

■ 1.2 ■ Origin of Linear Goal
Programming

Most constrained linear optimization models have an objective function that is expressed in terms of a single or uni-objective (e.g., cost minimization or profit maximization). This uni-objective characteristic limits the applicability of models, such as linear programming, to uni-objective problem situations. The "real world" environment, though, contains many multi-objective problem situations. For example, in government, administrators allocate budget dollars to accomplish multiple objectives in such areas as health, education and the military. Many problem situations involve not only multiple objectives but multiple conflicting objectives. For example, within an organization, budget allocations between departments sometimes conflict because department (as opposed to organizational) goals conflict. To resolve these types of problems, the mathematical programming technique of LGP was developed. LGP is an extension of linear programming, that is, capable of solving multiple-objective and conflicting-goal linear programming problems.

3

Many authors claim the origin of the linear goal programming analysis starts with G. B. Dantzig's 1947 interactive procedure. Dantzig's linear programming solution procedure provides the basis on which many of the LGP solution procedures originate. This origin may be appropriate, but it does not focus clearly on the specific nature of what is known today as LGP. It was not until 1961 that the name "goal programming" was attached to an analytical process that solved multiple objective linear programming problems.

One of the more significant contributions that stimulated interest in the application of LGP was a text written by A. Charnes and W. W. Cooper, *Management Models and Industrial Applications of Linear Programming* (1961; New York: John Wiley & Sons, Inc.). This text introduced the concept of LGP as an approach to dealing with unsolvable linear programming problems. Additionally, the text discussed the issue of goal attainment and the value of LGP in allowing for goals to be flexibly included in the model formulation.

Another contribution during the 1960s that had a significant impact on the formulation of LGP models was contained in a text written by Y. Ijiri, *Management Goals and Accounting for Control* (1965; Chicago: Rand McNally). Ijiri further developed the LGP foundation laid by Charnes and Cooper. He described the use of "preemptive priority factors" to model multiple conflicting objectives in accordance with their ranked importance in the objective function. Ijiri also suggested the "generalized inverse approach" as a solution method, and in doing so, established LGP as a distinct mathematical programming technique in the field of operations research.

It was not until the end of the 1960s and the early 1970s that LGP began receiving wide acclaim as a decision-making tool. The primary contributions in the 1970s have been applications oriented rather than model development oriented. A text written by Sang M. Lee, *Goal Programming for Decision Analysis* (1972; Philadelphia: Auerback Publishers, Inc.), illustrated the applied orientation characteristic of the period and significantly contributed to the continued growth in the use of LGP. Lee's text described the use of a modified simplex method for solving LGP problems and also provided a computer program which he developed. The availability of this computer program allowed for greater application of LGP to large-scale problems. Lee's text provided the basis on which goal programming became a management tool of decision science.

In the late 1970's and early 1980's the emphasis has more evenly been shared between *application* and *model development*. The applications focus more on the use of LGP as a decision modeling device which allows for considerable judgemental opinion and nonquantitatively derived information to be incorporated into the decision process. An excellent example of this type of LGP application is contained in Sang M. Lee's text *Management by Multiple Objectives* (1980; New York: Petrocelli). In this text, Lee describes how LGP can be used as an approach in modeling organizational type problems.

LGP model developments made during this time consisted basically of improvements in assessing the LGP model parameters and solution procedures. New LGP solution procedures have emerged that significantly reduce the size of the solution matrix necessary to solve LGP problems. This permits LGP problems to be solved more quickly and on smaller computer systems, such as micro computers. One of these recently proposed "reduced element" solution procedures will be presented in Chapter 4. Another recent example of a reduced solution matrix approach has been presented in a text by J. P. Ignizio, *Linear Programming in Single and Multiple Objective Systems* (1982; Englewood Cliffs, New Jersey: Prentice-Hall, Inc.). In this text, Ignizio describes the use of a "reflected p-space" that significantly reduces the size of solution matrix elements, thus reducing the need for unnecessary computation.

■ 1.3. ■ Literature Review

In addition to these researchers, many individuals over the years have conducted considerable research on the subject of LGP. Some of these research studies combine LGP with other operations research techniques. Some research studies apply LGP as a decision aid solely to a specific functional area within an organization, while other studies have been applied generally to any functional area or industry. Over 20 years of publications exist on LGP and are available to interested students. The availability of such research should encourage students to not try and "reinvent the wheel," but rather explore existing research. It may be that current problem situations have already been solved or modeled in the abundance of prior publications.

To aid students in the location and reference of these prior publications a bibliography of goal programming is now presented. This bibliography is extensive but not totally comprehensive. A histogram of the number of publication citations listed in the bibliography, by year, emphasizes the dramatic increase of interest in goal programming in recent years. This histogram is presented in Figure 1.1. It lists goal programming publications from 1970 through most of 1983. For publications prior to 1970, students are encouraged to review the bibliographies contained in several publications.[1]

The bibliography is designed to offer students an opportunity to be exposed to some prior LGP research. Specifically, the bibliography is to help students identify

---

1. Cochrane, J. and M. Zeleny (eds.), *Multiple Criteria Decision Making,* Columbia, South Carolina: University of South Carolina Press, 1973; Ignizio, J.P., "A Review of Goal Programming: A Tool for Multi-objective Analysis," *Journal of Operational Research Society,* 29 (November, 1978), pp. 1109–1119; Ignizio, J.P. *Goal Programming and Extensions,* Lexington, Mass.: Lexington Books, 1976; Kornbluth, J.S.H., "A Survey of Goal Programming," *OMEGA,* Vol. 1 (April, 1975), pp. 193–205; Starr, M.K. and M. Zeleny (eds.), *Multiple Criteria Decision Making,* New York: North-Holland Publishing Company, 1977.

Figure 1.1 Histogram of Goal Programming Publications From 1970 to 1982*

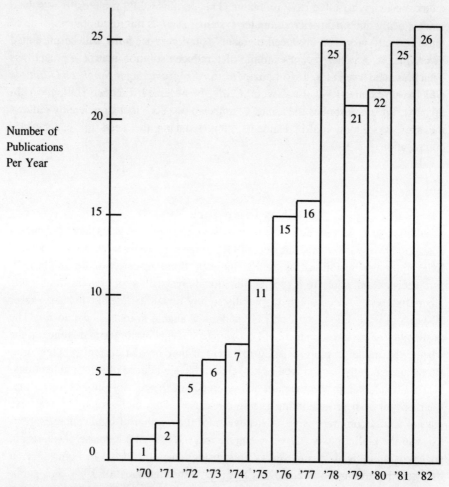

*Based on the bibliography presented in Section 1.3 which may not be a totally inclusive sample of all goal programming publications.

and reference relevant research expeditiously. To this end, it categorizes the LGP publications by their application to a specific business function (i.e., Accounting, Finance, Management and Marketing) and by their application in the service industries of Health, Education and the Military. These seven categories were selected on the basis of their prevalence in the applications observed in the more than 190 research studies listed in the bibliography. An additional category of Miscellaneous is also included for research studies that could not be placed into the other seven categories. This Miscellaneous category not only includes applications but also theory and methodological research studies. The theory and methodological studies are related to new LGP solution procedures, modeling improvements and conceptual information. Students are encouraged to reference these studies extensively. Students are also encouraged to use the other seven categories as they work through each case in PART II. Within each of the eight categories, the publications are alphabetized by author.

Since the publications have been categorized by application, it may be possible that a model can apply to more than one functional business area or service industry. Students should review all relevant category listings to maximize the benefit provided by this bibliography.

■ *Accounting Related References*

Blocker, J., "Sampling for Integrated Audit Objectives: A Comment," *The Accounting Review,* Vol. 53, (July, 1978), pp. 776–782.

Charnes, A.; Cooper, W.W.; Colantoni, C.; and Kortanek, K.O., "Economic, Social and Enterprise Accounting and Mathematical Models," *The Accounting Review,* Vol. 47, (January, 1972), pp. 85–108.

Jones, R.G., "Analyzing Initial and Growth Financing for Small Businesses," *Management Accounting,* Vol. 61, No. 5, (November, 1979), pp. 30–34, 38.

Killough, L.N., and Sounders, T.L., "A Goal Programming Model for Public Accounting Firms," *The Accounting Review,* Vol. 48, (April, 1973), pp. 268–279.

Lin, W.T., "Application of Goal Programming in Accounting," *Journal of Business Finance and Accounting,* Vol. 6, No. 4 (Winter, 1979), pp. 559–577.

Lin, W.T., "An Accounting Control System Structured on Multiple Objective Planning Models," *OMEGA,* Vol. 8, No. 3, (1980), pp. 375–382.

Lin, W.T., "Multiple Objective Budgeting Models: A Simulation," *Accounting Review,* Vol. 53, No. 1, (January 1978), pp. 61–76.

Olve, N., "Budgeting Design and Organizational Capabilities: Multicriterion Planning of Telephone Services," *OMEGA,* Vol. 9, No. 6, (1981), pp. 571–578.

Sheshai, K.M.; Harwood, G.B.; and Harmanison, R.H., "Cost Volume Profit Analysis with Integer Goal Programming," *Management Accounting,* Vol. 59, No. 4, (October, 1977), pp. 43–47.

Welling, P., "A Goal Programming Model for Human Resource Accounting in a CPA Firm," *Accounting, Organization and Society,* Vol. 2, (April, 1977), pp. 307–316.

■ *Finance Related References*

Booth, G.G., and Dash, G.H., "Bank Portfolio Management Using Non-linear Goal Programming," *The Financial Review*, Vol. 12, (Spring, 1977), pp. 59–69.

Callahan, J., "An Introduction to Financial Planning Through Goal Programming," *Cost and Management*, Vol. 3, No. 1, (January, 1973), pp. 7–12.

Caplin, D.A., and Kornbluth, J.S.H., "Multiobjective Investment Planning Under Certainty," *OMEGA*, Vol. 3, No. 4, (August, 1975), pp. 423–441.

De, P.K.; Acharya, D.; and Sahu, K.C., "A Chance-Constrained Goal Programming Model for Capital Budgeting," *Journal of the Operational Research Society*, Vol. 33, No. 7, (July, 1982), pp. 635–638.

Drandell, M., "A Resource Association Model for Insurance Management Utilizing Goal Programming," *Journal of Risk and Insurance*, Vol. 44, No. 2, (June, 1977), pp. 311–315.

Fortson, J.C., and Dince, R.R., "An Application of Goal Programming to Management of a Country Bank," *Journal of Bank Research*, Vol. 7, No. 4, (Winter, 1977), pp. 311–319.

Gleason, J.M., and Lilly, C.C., "A Goal Programming Model for Insurance Agency Management," *Decision Sciences*, Vol. 8, No. 1, (January, 1977), pp. 180–190.

Hawkins, C.A., and Adams, R.A., "A Goal Programming Model for Capital-Budgeting," *Financial Management*, Vol. 3, No. 1, (Spring, 1974), pp. 52–57.

Hons, H.K., "Finance Mix and Capital Structure," *Journal of Business Finance and Accounting*, Vol. 8, No. 4, (Winter, 1981), pp. 485–491.

Hsu, J.I.S., "The Goal Programming Approach to Investment Decision-Making," *Marquette Business Review*, Vol. 20, No. 4, (Winter, 1976), pp. 166–170.

Ignizio, J.P., "An Approach to the Capital Budgeting Problem with Multiple Objectives," *Engineering Economist*, Vol. 21, No. 4, (Summer, 1976), pp. 259–272.

Joiner, C., and Drake, A.E., "Governmental Planning and Budgeting with Multiple Objectives Models," *OMEGA*, Vol. 11, No. 1, (1983), pp. 57–66.

Keown, A.J., and Martin, J.D., "A Chance-Constrained Goal Programming Model for Working Capital Management," *Engineering Economist*, Vol. 22, No. 3, (Spring, 1977), pp. 153–174.

Keown, A.J., and Taylor, B.W., "A Chance-Constrained Integer Goal Programming Model for Capital Budgeting in the Production Area," *Journal of the Operational Research Society*, Vol. 31, No. 7, (July, 1980), pp. 579–589.

Keown, A.J.; Taylor, B.W.; and Duncan, C.P., "Allocation of Research and Development Funds: A Zero-One Goal Programming Approach," *OMEGA*. Vol. 7, No. 4, (1979), pp. 345–351.

Kornbluth, J.S.H., and Vinso, J.D., "Capital Structure and the Financing of the Multinational Approach: A Fractional Multiobjective Approach," *Journal of Financial and Quantitative Analysis,* Vol. 17, No. 2, (June, 1982), pp. 147–178.

Kramli, A.H., "Financial Planning Using Goal Programming," *OMEGA,* Vol. 8, No. 2, (1980), pp. 207–218.

Kumar, P.C., and Philippatos, G.C., "Conflict Resolution in Investment Decision: Implementation of Goal Programming Methodology for Dual-Purpose Funds," *Decision Sciences,* Vol. 10, No. 4, (October, 1979), pp. 562–576.

Kumar, P.C.; Philippatos, G.C.; and Ezzell, J.R., "Goal Programming and the Selection of Portfolios by Dual-Purpose Funds," *Journal of Finance,* Vol. 33, No. 1, (March, 1978), pp. 303–310.

Kvanli, A.H., "Financial Planning Using Goal Programming," *OMEGA,* Vol. 8, No. 1, (1980), pp. 207–218.

Lawrence, K.D., and Reeves, G.R., "A Zero-One Goal Programming Model for Capital Budgeting in a Property and Liability Insurance Company," *Computers and Operations Research,* Vol. 9, No. 4, (1982), pp. 303–309.

Lee, S.M., and Chesser, D.L., "Goal Programming for Portfolio Selection," *Journal of Portfolio Management,* Vol. 6, No. 3 (Spring, 1980), pp. 22–26.

Lee, S.M., and Terro, A.J., "Capital-Budgeting for Multiple Objectives," *Financial Management,* Vol. 3, No. 1, (Spring, 1974), pp. 58–66.

Lee, S.M., and Terro, A.J., "Optimizing the Portfolio Selection for Mutual Funds," *The Journal of Finance,* Vol. 28, No. 5, (December, 1973), pp. 1087–1101.

Leinbach, T.R., and Cromley, R.G., "A Goal Programming Approach to Public Investment Decisions: A Case Study of Rural Roads in Indonesia," *Socio Economic Planning Sciences,* Vol. 17, No. 1, (1983), pp. 1–10.

Lilly, C.C., and Gleason, J.M., "Implications of Goals Programming for Insurance Agency Decision Making," *OMEGA,* Vol. 4, No. 3, (1976), pp. 353–354.

Linke, C.M., and Whitford, D.T., "A Multiobjective Financial Planning Model for Electric Utility Rate Regulation," *Journal of Economics & Business,* Vol. 35, No. 3, (August, 1983), pp. 313–330.

Orne, D.L.; Rao, A.; and Wallace, W.W., "Profit Maximization with the Aid of Goal Programming for Speculative Housing Estate Developers," *Operational Research Quarterly,* Vol. 26, No. 4, (December 2, 1975), pp. 813–826.

Sartoris, W.L., and Spruill, M.L., "Goal Programming and Working-Capital Management," *Financial Management,* Vol. 3, No. 1, (Spring, 1974), pp. 67–74.

Sealey, C.W., "Commercial Bank Portfolio Management with Multiple Objectives," *Journal of Commercial Bank Lending,* Vol. 59, No. 6, (February, 1977), pp. 39–48.

Sealey, C.W., "Financial Planning with Multiple Objectives," *Financial Management,* Vol. 7, No. 4, (Winter, 1978), pp. 17–23.

9

Stone, B.K., and Reback, R., "Constructing a Model for Managing Portfolio Revisions," *Journal of Bank Research,* Vol. 6, No. 1, (September, 1975), pp. 48–60.

Vinso, J.D., "Financial Planning for the Multinational Corporation with Multiple Goals," *Journal of International Business Studies,* Vol. 13, No. 3, (Winter, 1982), pp. 43–58.

Walker, M.C., and Chandler, G.G., "Equitable Allocation of Credit Union Net Revenues—Goal Programming Approach," *Journal of Economics and Business,* Vol. 31, No. 1, (1978), pp. 63–39.

Wilstead, W.D.; Hendrick, T.E.; and Stewart, T.R., "Judgment Policy Capturing for Bank Loan Decisions: An Approach to Developing Objective Functions for Goal Programming Models," *Journal of Management Studies,* Vol. 12, No. 2, (May, 1975), pp. 210–225.

■ *Management Related References*

Arcelus, F.J., and Schaefer, N.V., "Social Demands as Stategic Issues: Some Conceptual Problems," *Strategic Management Journal,* Vol. 3, No. 4, (December, 1982), pp. 347–357.

Arthur, J.L., and Lawrence, K.D., "Multiple Goal Production and Logistics Planning in a Chemical and Pharmaceutical Company," *Computers and Operations Research,* Vol. 9, No. 2, (1982), pp. 127–137.

Arthur, J.L., and Lawrence, K.D., "A Multiple Goal Blending Problem," *Computer and Operations Research,* Vol. 7, No. 3, (1980), pp. 215–224.

Bazaraa, M.S., and Bouzaher, A., "A Linear Goal Programming Model for Developing Economics with an Illustration from the Agricultural Sector in Egypt," *Management Science,* Vol. 27, No. 4, (April, 1981), pp. 396–413.

Bottoms, M., and Bartlett, B., "Resource Allocation through Goal Programming," *Journal of Range Management,* Vol. 28, No. 3, (1975), pp. 442–447.

Budavei, V., "The Program-Goal Method of National Economic Planning," *International Studies of Management and Organization,* Vol. 11, No. 3–4, (Fall, 1981/Winter, 1982), pp. 142–156.

Deckro, R.F.; Hebert, J.E.; and Winkofsky, E.P., "Multiple Criteria Job-Shop Scheduling," *Computers and Operations Research,* Vol. 9, No. 4, (1982), pp. 279–285.

Dusansky, R., and Kalman, D.J., "Regional Multi-Objective Planning Under Uncertainty," *Regional Science and Urban Economics,* Vol. 11, No. 1, (February, 1981), pp. 121–134.

Eilon, S., "Multi-Criteria Warehouse Location," *International Journal of Physical Distribution and Materials Management,* Vol. 12, No. 1, (1982), pp. 42–45.

Fisk, J.C., "A Goal Programming Model for Output Planning," *Decision Sciences,* Vol. 10, No. 4, (October, 1979), pp. 593–603.

Goodman, D., "A Goal Programming Approach to Aggregate Planning of Production and Work-Force," *Management Science,* Vol. 20, No. 12, (August, 1974), pp. 1569–1575.

Green, G.I.; Kim, C.S.; and Lee, S.M., "A Multicriteria Warehouse Location Model," *International Journal of Physical Distribution and Materials Management,* Vol. 11, No. 1, (1981), pp. 5–13.

Green, M.K.; McCarthy, P., and Pearl, "Multi-Objective Allocation," *OMEGA,* Vol. 11, No. 2, (1983), pp. 195–200.

Hannan, E.L., "Application of Goal Programming Techniques to CPM Problems," *Socio-Economic Planning Sciences,* Vol. 12, No. 5, (1978), pp. 267–270.

Henderson, J.C., "Integrated Approach for Manpower Planning in the Service Sector," *OMEGA,* Vol. 10, No. 1, (1982), pp. 61–73.

Hershauer, J.C., and Gowens, J.W., "Machine Scheduling with Mixed Integer Goal Programming," *OMEGA,* Vol. 5, No. 5, (1977), p. 609.

Kalro, A.H.; Chaturvedi, G.; and Sengupta, S., "A Note on Goal Programming Approach to a Type of Quality Control Problem/Reply," *Journal of the Operational Research Society,* Vol. 34, No. 5, (May, 1983), pp. 437–440.

Keown, A.J., and Taylor, B.W., "Integer Goal Programming Model for the Implementation of Multiple Corporate Objectives," *Journal of Business Research,* Vol. 6, No. 3, (August, 1978), pp. 221–235.

King, A.S., "A Programming Procedure for Evaluating Personnel Policies," *Personnel Administration,* Vol. 27, No. 9, (September, 1982), pp. 82–95.

Kinory, S., "Goal Programming and Managerial Decision-Making," *Management International Review,* Vol. 18, No. 2, (1978), pp. 101–109.

Kwak, N.K.; Allen, T.D.; and Schniederjans, M.J., "A Multilevel Salary Compensation Model Using Goal Programming," *Recherche Operationnelle,* Vol. 16, No. 1, (1982), pp. 21–31.

Kwak, N.K., and Schniederjans, M.J., "A Goal Programming Model for Improved Transportation Problem Solutions," *OMEGA,* Vol. 7, No. 4, (1979), pp. 367–370.

Lawrence, K.D., and Burbridge, J.J., "A Multiple Goal Programming Model for the Coordinated Production and Logistics Planning," *International Journal of Production Research,* Vol. 14, No. 2, (1976), pp. 237–244.

Lee, S.M.; Clayton, E.R.; and Taylor, B.W., "A Goal Programming Approach to Multi-Period Production Line Scheduling," *Computers and Operations Research,* Vol. 5, No. 3, (1978), pp. 205–211.

Lee, S.M.; Franz, L.S.; and Wynne, A.J., "Optimizing State Patrol Manpower Allocations," *Journal of the Operational Research Society,* Vol. 30, No. 10, (October, 1979), pp. 885–896.

Lee, S.M.; Green, G.I.; and Kim, C.I., "A Multiple Criteria Model for the Location-Allocation Problem," *Computers and Operations Research,* Vol. 8, No. 1, (1981), pp. 1–8.

Lee, S.M.; Luthans, F.; and Olson, D.L., "A Management Science Approach to Contingency Models of Organizational Structure," *Academy of Management Journal,* Vol. 25, No. 3, (September, 1982), pp. 553–566.

Lee, S.M., and Schniederjans, M.J., "A Multi-Criteria Assignment Problem: A Goal Programming Approach," *Interfaces,* Vol. 13, No. 4, (August, 1983), pp. 75–81.

Lee, S.M., and Sevebeck, W., "An Aggregative Model for Municipal Economic Planning," *Policy Sciences,* Vol. 2, No. 2, (June, 1971), pp. 99–115.

Lee, S.M., and Wilkins, S.J., "Computer Facility Centralization/Decentralization: A Multiobjective Analysis Model," *Computers and Operations Research,* Vol. 10, No. 1, (1983), pp. 29–40.

Loucks, D.P., "An Application of Interactive Multiobjective Water Resources Planning," *Interfaces,* Vol. 8, No. 1, Part 1, (November, 1977), pp. 70–75.

Moore, L.J.; Taylor, B.W.; and Lee, S.M., "Analysis of a Transshipment Problem with Multiple Conflicting Objectives," *Computers and Operations Research,* Vol. 5, No. 1, (1978), pp. 39–46.

Neely, W.P.; Sellers, J.; and North, R.M., "Goal Programming Priority Sensitivity Analysis: An Application in Natural Resource Decision Making Processes," *Interfaces,* Vol. 10, No. 5, (October, 1980), pp. 83–89.

Nelson, M., "Application of Management Science to Water Resource Planning in Latin America," *European Journal of Operational Research,* Vol. 3, No. 1, (January, 1979), pp. 6–12.

Nijkamp, P., and Spronk, J., "Analysis of Production and Location Decisions by Means of Multi-Criteria Analysis," *Engineering and Process Economics,* Vol. 42, No. 3, (June, 1979), pp. 285–302.

Osleeb, J.P., and Ratick, S.J., "A Mixed Integer and Multiple Objective Programming Model to Analyze Coal Handling in New England," *European Journal of Operational Research,* Vol. 12, No. 3, (March, 1983), pp. 302–313.

Parker, B.R., and Kaluzny, A.D., "Design Planning to Meet Goals in Human Service Organizations," *Human Systems Management,* Vol. 3, No. 2, (June, 1982), pp. 77–90.

Price, W.L., "A Review of Mathematical Models in Human Resources Planning," *OMEGA,* Vol. 8, No. 6, (1980), pp. 639–645.

Price, W.L., "Solving Goal-Programming Manpower Models Using Advanced Network Codes," *Journal of the Operational Research Society,* Vol. 29, No. 12, (December, 1978), pp. 1231–1239.

Rifai, A.K., "The Role of Mathematical Programming in Allocating Scarce Resources: The Case of Multiple Goals," *Industrial Management,* Vol. 20, No. 4, (July–August, 1978), pp. 1–3.

Saladin, B.A., "Goal Programming Applied to Police Patrol Allocation," *Journal of Operations Management,* Vol. 2, No. 4, (August, 1982), pp. 239–249.

Salvia, A.A., and Ludwig, W.R., "Application of Goal Programming at Lord Corporation," *Interfaces,* Vol. 9, No. 4, (1979), pp. 129–133.

Samouilidis, J.E., and Pappas, I.A., "A Goal Programming Approach to Energy Forecasting," *European Journal of Operational Research,"* Vol. 5, No. 5, (November, 1980), pp. 321–331.

Schniederjans, M.J.; Kwak, N.K.; and Helmer, M.C., "An Application of Goal Programming to Resolve a Site Location Problem," *Interfaces,* Vol. 12, No. 3, (June, 1982), pp. 65–72.

Sengupta, S., "Goal Programming Approach to a Type of Quality Control Problem," *Journal of the Operational Research Society,* Vol. 32, No. 3, (March, 1981), pp. 207–211.

Taylor, B.W., "Urban Recreational Planning: A Proposed Methodology," *OMEGA,* Vol. 5, No. 5 (1977), pp. 618–619.

Taylor, B.W., and Keown, A.J., "Goal Programming Application of Capital Project Selection in Production Area," *AIIE Transactions,* Vol. 10, No. 1, (1978), pp. 52–57.

Taylor, B.W., and Keown, A.J., "Planning Urban Recreational Facilities with Integer Goal Programming," *Journal of the Operational Research Society,* Vol. 29, No. 8, (August, 1978), pp. 751–758.

Taylor, B.W.; Moore, L.J.; and Clayton, E.R., "R&D Project Selection and Manpower Allocation with Integer Nonlinear Goal Programming," *Management Science,* Vol. 28, No. 10, (October, 1982), pp. 1149–1158.

Tersine, R.J., "Organizational Objectives and Goal Programming: A Convergence," *Managerial Planning,* Vol. 25, No. 2, (September/October, 1976), pp. 27–32 + .

Welam, U.P., "Comments on Goal Programming for Aggregate Planning," *Management Science,* Vol. 22, No. 6, (February, 1976), pp. 708–712.

Wheeler, B.M., and Russell, J.R.M., "Goal Programming and Agricultural Planning," *Operational Research Quarterly,* Vol. 28, No. 1, (1977), pp. 21–32.

Zanakis, S.H., and Maret, M.W., "A Markovian Goal Programming Approach to Aggregate Manpower Planning," *Journal of the Operational Research Society,* Vol. 32, No. 1, (January, 1981), pp. 55–63.

■ *Marketing Related References*

De Kluyver, C.A., "An Exploration of Various Goal Programming Formulations—with Application to Advertising Media Scheduling," *Journal of the Operational Research Society,* Vol. 30, No. 2, (February, 1979), pp. 167–171.

De Kluyver, C.A., "Hard and Soft Constraints in Media Scheduling," *Journal of Advertising Research,* Vol. 18, No. 3, (June, 1978), pp. 27–31.

Keown, A.J., and Duncan, C.P., "Integer Goal Programming in Advertising Media Selection," *Decision Sciences,* Vol. 10, No. 4, (October, 1979), pp. 577–592.

Kim, C. I., "A Manufacturer's Retail Store Selection Model in the Normative Distribution Channel Design: A Goal Programming Approach," *Akron*

Business & Economic Review, Vol. 14, No. 3, (Fall, 1983), pp. 41–47.

Lee, S.M., and Bird, M., "A Goal Programming Model for Sales Effort Allocation," *Business Perspectives,* Vol. 6, (Summer, 1970), pp. 17–21.

Lee, S.M., and Nicely, R.E., "Goal Programming for Marketing Decisions—A Case Study," *Journal of Marketing,* Vol. 38, No. 1, (January, 1974), pp. 24–32.

Mehta, A.J., and Rifai, A.K., "Goal Programming Application to Assignment Problem in Marketing," *Journal of the Academy of Marketing Science,* Vol. 7, No. 1, 2, (Winter/Spring, 1979), pp. 108–116.

Taylor, B.W., and Anderson, P.F., "Goal Programming Approach to Marketing/ Production Planning," *Industrial Marketing Management,* Vol. 8, No. 2, (April, 1979), pp. 136–144.

Wilson, J.M., "The Handling of Goals in Marketing Problems," *Management Decision,* Vol. 13, No. 3, (1975), pp. 175–180.

■ Health Related References

Anderson, A.M., and Earle, M.D., "Diet Planning in the Third World by Linear and Goal Programming," *Journal of the Operational Research Society,* Vol. 34, No. 1, (January, 1983), pp. 9–13.

Arthur, J.L., and Ravindran, A., "A Multiple Objective Nurse Scheduling Problem," *AIIE Transactions,* Vol. 13, No. 1, (March, 1981), pp. 55–60.

Benito, M.A., and Devaux, P., "Location and Size of Day Nurseries—A Multiple Goal Approach," *European Journal of Operational Research,* Vol. 6, No. 2, (February 1981), pp. 195–198.

Charnes, A.; Cooper, W.W.; Karwan, K.R.; and Wallace, W.A., "A Chance-Constrained Goal Programming Model to Evaluate Response Resources for Marine Pollution Disasters," *Journal of Environmental Economics and Management,* Vol. 6, No. 3, (September, 1979), pp. 244–274.

Charnes, A.; Cooper, W.W.; Karwan, K.R.; and Wallace, W.A., "A Goal Interval Programming Model for Resource Allocation in a Marine Environmental Protection Program," *Journal of Environmental Economy and Management,* Vol. 3, No. 4, (December, 1976), pp. 347–362.

Charnes, A., and Storbeck, C.J., "A Goal Programming Model for the Siting of Multilevel EMS Systems," *Socio-Economic Planning Sciences,* Vol. 14, No. 4, (1980), pp. 155–161.

Jackman, H.W., "Financing Public Hospitals in Ontario—A Case Study in Rationing of Capital Budgets," *Management Science,* Vol. 20, No. 4, Part 2, (December, 1973), pp. 645–655.

Jones, L., and Kwak, N.K., "A Goal Programming Model for Allocating Human Resources for the Good Laboratory Practice Regulations," *Decision Sciences,* Vol. 13, No. 1, (January, 1982), pp. 156–166.

Kendall, K.E., and Lee, S.M., "Formulating Blood Rotation Policies with Multiple Objectives," *Management Science,* Vol. 26, No. 11, (November, 1980), pp. 1145–1157.

Kendall, K.E., and Lee, S.M., "Improving Perishable Product Inventory Management Using Goal Programming," *Journal of Operations Management,* Vol. 1, No. 2, (November, 1980), pp. 77–84.

Keown, A.J., and Martin, J.D., "An Integer Goal Programming Model for Capital Budgeting in Hospitals," *Financial Management,* Vol. 5, No. 3, (Autumn, 1976), pp. 28–35.

Trivedi, V.M., "A Mixed-Integer Goal Programming Model for Nursing Service Budgeting," *Operations Research,* Vol. 29, No. 5, (September/October, 1981), pp. 1019–1034.

Taylor, B.W.; Davis, K.R.; and Ryan, L.J., "Compliance with the Occupational Safety and Health Act: A Mathematical Programming Network," *Decision Sciences,* Vol. 8, No. 4, (October, 1977), pp. 677–691.

Wacht, R.F., and Whitford, D.T., "A Goal Programming Model for Capital Investment Analysis in Nonprofit Hospitals," *Financial Management,* Vol. 5, No. 2, (Summer, 1976), pp. 37–47.

■ *Education Related References*

Franz, L.S.; Lee, S.M.; and Van Horn, J.C., "An Adaptive Decision Support System for Academic Resource Planning, *Decision Sciences,* Vol. 12, No. 2, (April, 1981), pp. 276–293.

Harwood, G.B., and Lawless, R.W., "Optimizing Faculty Teaching Schedules," *Decision Sciences,* Vol. 6, No. 3, (July, 1975), pp. 513–524.

Joiner, C., "Academic Planning Through the Goal Programming Model," *Interfaces,* Vol. 10, No. 4, (August, 1980), pp. 86–92.

Kendall, K.E., and Luebbe, R.L., "Management of College Student Recruiting Activities Using Goal Programming," *Decision Sciences,* Vol. 12, No. 2, (April, 1981), pp. 193–205.

Keown, A.J.; Taylor, B.W.; and Pinkerton, J.M., "Multiple Objective Capital Budgeting Within the University," *Computers and Operations Research,* Vol. 8, No. 2, (1981), pp. 59–70.

Knutson, D.L.; Marquis, L.M.; Ricchiute, D.N.; and Saunders, G.J., "A Goal-Programming Model for Achieving Racial Balance in Public Schools," *Socio-Economic Planning Sciences,* Vol. 14, No. 3, (1980), pp. 109–116.

Lee, S.M. and Clayton, E., "A Goal Programming Model for Academic Resource Allocation," *Management Science,* Vol. 18, No. 8, (April, 1972), pp. 390–408.

Lee, S.M., and Moore, L.J., "Optimizing University Admissions Planning," *Decision Sciences,* Vol. 5, No. 4, (1974), pp. 405–414.

Lee, S.M., and Moore, L.J., "Multi-Criteria School Busing Models," *Management Science,* Vol. 23, No. 7, (March, 1977), pp. 703–715.

Ritzman, L.; Bradford, J.; and Jacobs, R., "A Multiple Objective Approach to Space Planning for Academic Facilities," *Management Science,* Vol. 25, No. 9, (September, 1979), pp. 895–906.

Saunders, G.J., "An Application of Goal Programming to the Desegregation Busing Problem," *Socio-Economic Planning Sciences,* Vol. 15, No. 6, (1981), pp. 291–294.

Schroeder, R.G., "Resource Planning In University Management by Goal Programming," *Operations Research,* Vol. 22, No. 4, (January/April, 1974), pp. 700–710.

Smith, L.D., "Planning Models for Budgeting Teaching Resources," *OMEGA,* Vol. 6, No. 1, (1978), pp. 83–88.

Walters, A; Mangold, J.; and Haran, E., "A Comprehensive Planning Model for Long-Range Academic Strategies," *Management Science,* Vol. 22, No. 7, (March, 1976), pp. 727–738.

■ Military Related References

Armstrong, R.D., and Cook, W.D., "Goal Programming Models for Assigning Search and Rescue Aircraft to Bases," *Journal of the Operational Research Society,* Vol. 30, No. 6, (June, 1979), pp. 555–561.

Bres, E.S.; Burns, D.; Charnes, A.; and Cooper, W.W., "A Goal Programming Model for Planning Officer Accessions," *Management Science,* Vol. 26, No. 8, (August, 1980), pp. 773–783.

Collins, R.W.; Gass, S.I.; and Rosendahl, E.E., "The ASCAR Model for Evaluating Military Manpower Policy," *Interfaces,* Vol. 13, No. 3, (June, 1983), pp. 44–53.

Mellichamp, J.M.; Dixon, W.L.; and Mitchell, S.L., "Ballistic Missile Defense Technology Management with Goal Programming," *Interfaces,* Vol. 10, No. 5, (October, 1980), pp. 68–75.

Nussbaum, D.A., "Goal Programming as an Aid to Resource Management," *Defense Systems Management Review,* Vol. 3, No. 2, (Spring, 1980), pp. 28–33.

Sullivan, R.S., and Fitzsimmons, J.A., "Goal Programming—Model for Readiness and Optimal Redeployment of Resources," *Socio-Economic Planning Sciences,* Vol. 12, No. 5, (1978), pp. 215–220.

Taylor, B.W.; Keown, A.J.; and Greenwood, A.G., "An Integer Goal Programming Model for Determining Military Aircraft Expenditures," *Journal of the Operational Research Society,* Vol. 34, No. 5, (May, 1983), pp. 379–390.

■ Miscellaneous References

Arthur, J.L., and Ravindran, A., "An Efficient Goal Programming Algorithm Using Constraint Partitioning and Variable Elimination," *Management Science,* Vol. 24, No. 8, (April, 1978), p. 867–868.

Arthur, J.L., and Ravindran, A., "A Branch and Bound Algorithm with Constraint Partitioning for Integer Goal Programming Problems," *European Journal of Operational Research,* Vol. 4, No. 6, (June, 1980), pp. 421–425.

Awerbuch, S.; Ecker, J.G.; and Wallace, W.A., "Hidden Nonlinearities in the Application of Goal Programming," *Management Science,* Vol. 22, No. 8, (April, 1976), pp. 918–920.

Bajgier, S.M., and Hill, A.V., "An Experimental Comparison of Statistical and Linear Programming Approaches to the Discriminate Problem," *Decision Science,* Vol. 13, No. 4, (October, 1982), pp. 604–618.

Barnett, D.; Blake, B.; and McCash, B.A., "Goal Programming via Multidimensional Scaling Applied to Senegalese Subsistence Farms," *American Journal of Agricultural Economics,* Vol. 64, No. 4, (November, 1982), pp. 720–727.

Charnes, A., and Cooper, W.W., "Goal Programming and Constrained Regression—A Comment," *OMEGA,* Vol. 3, No. 4, (August, 1975), pp. 403–409.

Charnes, A.; Cooper, W.W.; Klingman, D.; and Niehaus, R.J., "Explicit Solutions in Convex Goal Programming," *Management Science,* Vol. 22, No. 4, (December, 1975), pp. 438–448.

Clayton, E.R., and Moore, L.J., "Goal vs. Linear Programming," *Journal of Systems Management,* Vol. 23, No. 11, (November, 1972), pp. 26–31.

Clayton, E.R.; Weber, W.E.; and Taylor, B.W., "A Goal Programming Approach to the Optimization of Multiresponse Simulation Models," *IIE Transactions,* Vol. 14, No. 4, (December, 1982), pp. 282–287.

Dauer, J.P., and Krueger, R.J., "An Iterative Approach to Goal Programming," *Operational Research Quarterly,* Vol. 28, No. 3, (1977), pp. 671–681.

Dyer, S., "Interactive Goal Programming," *Management Science,* Vol. 19, No. 1, (September, 1972), pp. 62–70.

Eilon, S., "Goals and Constraints in Decision-Making," *Operational Research Quarterly,* Vol. 23, No. 1, (March, 1972), pp. 3–16.

Flavell, R.B., "A New Goal Programming Formulation," *OMEGA,* Vol. 4, No. 6, (1976), pp. 731–732.

Freed, N., and Glover, F., "Simple but Powerful Goal Programming Models for Discriminant Problems," *European Journal of Operational Research,* Vol. 7, No. 1, (May, 1981), pp. 44–60.

Garrod, N.W., and Moores, B., "An Implicit Enumeration Algorithm for Solving Zero-One Goal Programming Problems," *OMEGA,* Vol. 6, No. 4, (1978), pp. 374–377.

Gibbs, T., "Goal Programming," *Journal of Systems Management,* Vol. 24, No. 5, (May, 1973), pp. 38–41.

Hannan, E.L., "A Graphical Interpretation in Goal Programming Problem," *OMEGA,* Vol. 4, No. 6, (1976), pp. 733–735.

Hannan, E.L., "On Fuzzy Goal Programming," *Decision Sciences,* Vol. 12, No. 3, (July, 1981), pp. 522–531.

Hannan, E.L., and Narasimhan, R., "On Fuzzy Goal Programming/On Fuzzy Goal Programming—Some Comments/Some Further Comments on Fuzzy Priorities," *Decision Sciences,* Vol. 12, No. 3, (July, 1981), pp. 522–541.

Hwang, C.L.; Paidy, S.R.; Yoon, K.; and Masud, A.S.M., "Mathematical Programming with Multiple Objectives: A Tutorial," *Computers and Operational Research,* Vol. 7, No. 1, 2, (1980), pp. 5–31.

Ignizio, J.P., "An Approach to the Modeling and Analysis of Multiobjective Generalized Networks," *European Journal of Operational Research,* Vol. 12, No. 4, (April, 1983), pp. 357–361.

Ignizio, J.P., "A Note on Computational Methods in Lexicographic Linear Goal Programming," *Journal of the Operational Research Society,* Vol. 34, No. 6, (June, 1983), pp. 539–542.

Ignizio, J.P., "A Review of Goal Programming—Tool for Multi-Objective Analysis," *Journal of the Operational Research Society,* Vol. 29, No. 11, (1978), pp. 1109–1119.

Ignizio, J.P., "The Determination of a Subset of Efficient Solutions Via Goal Programming," *Computers and Operations Research,* Vol. 8, No. 1, (1981), pp. 9–16.

Ignizio, J.P., "The Development of Cost Estimated Relationships Via Goal Programming," *Engineering Economist,* Vol. 24, No. 1, (Fall, 1978), pp. 37–47.

Ignizio, J.P., and Hannan, E.L., "On the (Re)Discovery of Fuzzy Goal Programming/Contrasting Fuzzy Goal Programming and "Fuzzy" Multicriteria Programming," *Decision Sciences,* Vol. 13, No. 2, (April, 1982), pp. 331–339.

Ignizio, J.P., and Perlis, J.H., "Sequential Linear Goal Programming: Implementation Via MPSX," *Computers and Operations Research,* Vol. 6, No. 3, (1979), pp. 141–145.

Kornbluth, J.S.H., "A Survey of Goal Programming," *OMEGA,* Vol. 1, (April, 1975), pp. 193–205.

Kornbluth, J.S.H., and Steuer, R.E., "Goal Programming with Linear Fractional Criteria," *European Journal of Operational Research,* Vol. 8, No. 1, (September, 1981), pp. 58–65.

Kornbluth, J.S.H., and Steuer, R.E., "Multiple Objective Linear Fractional Programming," *Management Science,* Vol. 27, No. 9, (September, 1981), pp. 1024–1039.

Lee, S.M., "Decision Analysis Through Goal Programming," *Decision Sciences,* Vol. 2, No. 1, (February, 1971), pp. 172–180.

Lee, S.M., "Goal Programming for Decision Analysis of Multiple Objectives," *Sloan Management Review,* Vol. 14, No. 2, (Summer, 1973), pp. 11–24.

Masud, A.S., and Hwang, C.L., "Interactive Sequential Goal Programming," *Journal of the Operational Research Society,* Vol. 32, No. 5, (May, 1981), pp. 391–400.

Mehta, A.J., and Rifai, A.K., "Application of Linear Programming vs. Goal Programming to Assignment Problem," *Akron Business and Economic Review,* Vol. 7, No. 4, (Winter, 1976), pp. 52–55.

Moore, L.J.; Taylor, B.W.; Clayton, E.R.; and Lee, S.M., "Analysis of a Multi-

Criteria Project Crashing Model," *AIIE Transactions*, Vol. 10, No. 2, (1978), pp. 163–169.

Narasimhan, R., "Goal Programming in a Fuzzy Environment," *Decision Sciences*, Vol. 11, No. 2, (April, 1980), pp. 325–336.

Ratick, S.J., "Multiobjective Programming with Related Bargaining Games," *Regional Science & Urban Economics*, Vol. 13, No. 1, (February, 1983), pp. 141–160.

Rifai, A.K., "Sensitivity Analysis of Linear Programming vs. Goal Programming," *Industrial Management*, Vol. 22, No. 1, (January–February, 1980), pp. 12–17.

Ringuest, J.L., and Gulledge, T.R., Jr., "A Preemptive Value-Function Method Approach for Multiobjective Linear Programming Problems," *Decision Sciences*, Vol. 14, No. 1, (January, 1983), pp. 76–86.

Rivett, P., "Multidimensional Scaling for Multiobjective Policies," *OMEGA*, Vol. 5, No. 4, (1977), pp. 367–379.

Rowe, M.D., and Pierce, B.L., "Some Tests of Analytical Multiobjective Decision-Making Methods," *Socio-Economic Planning Sciences*, Vol. 16, No. 3, (1982), pp. 133–140.

Schilling, D.A.; Revelle, C.; and Cohon, J., "An Approach to the Display and Analysis of Multiobjective Problems," *Socio Economic Planning Sciences*, Vol. 17, No. 2, (1983), pp. 57–63.

Schniederjans, M.J., and Kwak, N.K., "An Alternative Solution Method for Goal Programming Problems: A Tutorial," *Journal of the Operational Research Society*, Vol. 33, No. 3, (March, 1982), 247–251.

Seiford, L. and Yu, P.L., "Potential Solutions of Linear-Systems—Multi- Criteria Multiple Constraint Levels Program," *Journal of Mathematical Analysis and Applications*, Vol. 69, No. 2, (1979), pp. 283–303.

Selim, S.Z., and Rifai, A.K., "Constraint Partitioning and Variable Elimination in Goal Programming," *Industrial Management*, Vol. 24, No. 5, (September/ October, 1982), pp. 1–6.

Sharif, M.N., and Agarwal, R.L., "Solving Multicriterion Integer Programming Problems," *Industrial Management*, Vol. 18, No. 1, (January–February, 1976), pp. 17–23.

Sherali, H.D., "Equivalent Weights for Lexicographic Multi-Objective Programs: Characterization and Computations," *European Journal of Operational Research*, Vol. 11, No. 4, (December, 1982), pp. 367–379.

Shim, J.K., and Siegel, J., "Quadratic Preferences and Goal Programming," *Decision Sciences*, Vol. 6, No. 4, (October, 1975), pp. 662–669.

Smith, C.J., "Using Goal Programming to Determine Interest Group Disutility for Public Policy Choices," *Socio-Economic Planning Sciences*, Vol. 14, No. 3, (1980), pp. 117–120.

Spronk, J., and Veeneklaas, F., "A Feasibility Study of Economic and Environmental Scenarios by Means of Interactive Multiple Goal Programming,"

Regional Science & Urban Economics, Vol. 13, No. 1, (February, 1983), pp. 141–160.

Steuer, R.E., "Goal Programming Sensitivity Analysis Using Interval Penalty Weights," *Mathematical Programming,* Vol. 17, No. 1, (1979), pp. 16–31.

Stewart, T.J., "A Descriptive Approach to Multiple-Criteria Decision Making," *Journal of the Operational Research Society,* Vol. 32, No. 1, (January, 1981), pp. 45–53.

Walker, J., "An Interactive Method as an Aid in Solving Multi-Objective Mathematical Programming Problems," *European Journal of Operational Research,* Vol. 2, No. 5 (September, 1978), pp. 341–349.

Wallenius, H., "Optimizing Macroeconomic Policy: A Review of Approaches and Applications," *European Journal of Operational Research,* Vol. 10, No. 3, (July, 1982), pp. 221–228.

Werczberger, E., "Multi-Objective Linear Programming with Partial Ranking of Objectives," *Socio-Economic Planning Sciences,* Vol. 15, No. 6, (1981), pp. 331–340.

Widhelm, W.B., "Extensions of Goal Programming Models," *OMEGA,* Vol. 9, No. 2, (1981), pp. 212–214.

Wright, J.; Revelle, C.; and Cohon, J., "A Multiobjective Integer Programming Model for the Land Acquisition Problem," *Regional Science & Urban Economics,* Vol. 13, No. 1, (February, 1983), pp. 31–53.

■ 1.4 ■ Summary

The origins of many optimization procedures are unclear. In the case of LGP, most research historians would agree that this modeling device is little over 20 years old. There is no question that LGP is a modern decision making tool whose methodological and application potential is growing with the passage of time. In Chapter 2, we will learn how to use linear programming which is a prerequisite to understanding how LGP can be used as a decision-making tool.

KEY VOCABULARY

Linear goal programming

Multi-objective

Multiple conflicting objectives

Reflected p-space

Uni-objective

CHAPTER QUESTIONS

1.1 How does LGP differ from linear programming?

1.2 Trace the history of LGP from the early 1960s to the present. List the names of several major contributors to this field of study.

1.3 How would you describe the research activity on the subject of LGP? Is it presently in a decline or growth state? Explain your answer and offer evidence to support your opinion.

1.4 In the bibliography in this chapter, the LGP applications were sorted into four business function activities (i.e., accounting, finance, management and marketing). Which of these four functions has accumulated the greatest number of LGP applications and justify why this function should have more applications than the other functional areas.

1.5 In Miscellaneous References, can any additional service industry areas be defined? If so, develop a brief bibliography of your own listing all cited referenced under the additional service industry listings.

2
Prerequisite Linear Programming

■ 2.1 ■ Chapter Overview

This chapter presents linear programming formulation and solution procedures. A step-by-step formulation procedure is described for linear programming problems. In addition, this chapter presents solution procedures that can be used to solve maximization, minimization, and integer linear programming problems. Special solution procedure complications are also addressed in this chapter.

Since LGP is an extension of linear programming, linear programming concepts and methodology are an essential prerequisite to learning LGP. The purpose of this chapter is to provide students with extensive exposure to linear programming formulation and solution procedures which can be used as a basis to understanding LGP formulation and solution procedures.

■ 2.2 ■ Generalized Linear Programming Models

One of the most powerful decision-making tools available is linear programming. Linear programming is a mathematical technique. It is called linear programming because we use mathematical expressions to model or program a problem situation. Linear programming is referred to as a uni-objective constrained optimization technique. *Uni-objective* refers to linear programming's desire to seek a single objective of either maximizing or minimizing unknown variables in a model. These unknown

23

variables are usually profit related in a maximization problem and cost related in a minimization problem. Unfortunately, the maximization of profit or the minimization of cost is always constrained by real-world limitations of finite resources. Linear programming allows us an opportunity to combine the *constraining limitations* of the decision environment with the interaction of the unknown values we are seeking to *optimize*.

Linear programming has been applied to solving problems in all the primary business functions of accounting, finance, management and marketing. In accounting, linear programming has been used to assess cost information on resource utilization and evaluate auditing practices. Linear programming has been used in the finance function for planning investments in plant and equipment, portfolio management, and risk analysis. In management, linear programming has been used to solve problems in site location, physical plant layout, and human resource assignments. In marketing, it has been used to solve salesperson resource allocation problems as well as redistricting of sales territories.

Linear programming has also been used in service industries, such as health education and the military. Recent applications in these fields include nuclear energy waste utilization and treatment, forecasting faculty requirements in higher education and missile deployment planning. Many more examples exist, and students are encouraged to review the research on this subject area.

All linear programming models consist of three components: an objective function, side constraints and non-negativity requirements. Before examining each of these modeling components, several linear programming terms need to be defined.

■ Linear Programming Terminology

To fully understand any subject area, students should always acquaint themselves with unique terms and expressions used by people in that field of study. The following are definitions of several commonly used linear programming terms and expressions.

Decision Variables: A set of unknowns (i.e., represented in the linear programming model as x_j, where $j = 1, 2, \ldots, J$) we are seeking to determine.

Side Constraints: A set of constraints that express the relevant limitations or restrictions in the problem situation being modeled. These limitations or restrictions are necessary constraints upon the objective function.

Right-Hand-Side Values: Values that usually express resource values (i.e., represented by b_i) that we seek to fully utilize. The name of these values originates from their position on the right-hand side of the constraint.

Slack Variables: Variables that express the possibility of positive or negative deviation from a right-hand-side value (i.e., represented in a linear programming model as s_i, where $i = 1,2,. . .,I$ and I is the number of side constraints in the model).

Technological Coefficients: Numerical values (i.e., represented by a_{ij}) that express the per unit usage of the b_i for each x_j.

Z (value): An unknown value that we seek to optimize, either by maximization (i.e., making it as large as possible) or minimization (i.e., making it as small as possible).

Contribution Coefficients: Numerical values (i.e., represented by c_j) that express the per unit contribution to Z for each x_j.

Objective Function: A mathematical expression that equates Z with the sum of the product of all contribution coefficients times their respective decision variables.

Tableau: A specialized matrix of numbers used in the simplex solution procedure.

Basic Variables: A set of variables (i.e., either decision or slack variables) that exist in the Basis column of the simplex tableau.

Non-Basic Variables: All variables (i.e., either decision or slack variables) that are not in the Basis column of the simplex tableau. These variables are also called zero-variables because they are always equal to zero.

■ *Basic Elements*

Some linear programming problems are very complex, requiring a great deal of modeling, while some are small-scale, requiring little modeling effort. In this section, the basic modeling elements of linear programming are introduced. These modeling elements are in common with all sizes of linear programming problem formulations. The elements provide the common framework in which any unique problem situation can be expressed.

■ General Statement of the Linear Programming Model

As mentioned before, linear programming models seek a uni-objective of either maximizing or minimizing unknown variables. So, linear programming models are expressed in one of two different forms: maximization or minimization. We usually use the maximization model when trying to maximize profit or sales contribution. The minimization model is usually used when we want to find solutions to minimize costs or the use of productive resources. Both types of models can be expressed in a generalized form. The generalized models are presented to provide a framework to guide in the structuring of linear programming problems. The generalized model of a maximization problem can be stated as follows:

$$\text{Maximize:} \quad Z = \sum_{j=1}^{J} c_j x_j$$

$$\text{subject to:} \quad \sum_{j=1}^{J} a_{ij} x_j \lessgtr b_i \qquad \text{(for } i = 1, 2, \ldots, I)$$

$$\text{and} \qquad x_j \geq 0 \qquad \text{(for } j = 1, 2, \ldots, J)$$

where:

Z = value to be maximized (unknown)

c_j = contribution coefficients (given constants)

x_j = decision variables (unknown)

a_{ij} = technological coefficients (given constants)

b_i = right-hand-side values (given constants)

I = number of side constraints

J = number of decision variables

The generalized model for a minimization problem is quite similar to the maximization model. The generalized model for a minimization problem can be stated as follows:

$$\text{Minimize:} \quad Z = \sum_{j=1}^{J} c_j x_j$$

$$\text{subject to:} \quad \sum_{j=1}^{J} a_{ij} x_j \lessgtr b_i \qquad \text{(for } i = 1, 2, \ldots, I)$$

$$\text{and} \qquad x_j \geq 0 \qquad \text{(for } j = 1, 2, \ldots, J)$$

The only real difference between the two generalized models are the use of the words "maximize" and "minimize" and possibly the direction of the inequalities. In practice it is possible to have mixtures of $\leq$, $\geq$ and even $=$ signs in a single linear programming problem, regardless of whether the problem type is a maximization or minimization.

As mentioned before, there are three elements in common with both of these two types of models that are required in all linear programming models. These elements are called an *objective function, side constraints* and *non-negativity requirements*.

■ Objective Functions

There are two different types of linear programming objective functions. They can be expressed as follows:

$$\text{Maximize:} \quad Z = \sum_{j=1}^{J} c_j x_j \qquad \qquad \text{(2.1)}$$

$$\text{Minimize:} \quad Z = \sum_{j=1}^{J} c_j x_j \qquad (2.2)$$

In Equation 2.1, Z is the maximized value of the sum of the products of c_j times x_j. This objective function is used when we seek a maximized value of Z. In effect, this type of problem has a unitary goal of maximizing Z by selecting the values of x_j as large as possible. This type of objective function is used in profit maximizing problems. Equation 2.2 expresses an objective function where we minimize the value of Z. This type of objective function is used in a cost minimizing type problem. Which objective function is to be selected is dependent on the problem situation. Selection criteria of the objective function will be discussed in Section 2.3.

■ Side Constraints

There are three different types of side constraints that can be used in any type of linear programming problem. The three different types of side constraints are as follows:

$$\sum_{j=1}^{J} a_{ij} x_j \leq b_i \qquad (2.3)$$

$$\sum_{j=1}^{J} a_{ij} x_j \geq b_i \qquad (2.4)$$

$$\sum_{j=1}^{J} a_{ij} x_j = b_i \qquad (2.5)$$

The composition of the side constraints can best be explained by dividing the constraints into two parts: the left-hand-side of the constraint and the right-hand-side. The left-hand-side of the constraint in Equation 2.3 is made up of the sum of the products of the technological coefficients and their respective decision variables. The technological coefficients are the usage of the b_i right-hand-side value on an x_j per unit basis. The right-hand-side of the constraint will always consist of a single constant value that usually represents the total available resources (or other limiting factors) whose use is defined by the technological coefficients. Examples of right-hand-side values might be total available labor hours to produce furniture or total available tires per week to use in the production of automobiles. The technological coefficients in the left-hand-side of the constraints are referred to as *technological* because they reflect the utilization rates for resources. Since technological advances usually alter resource utilization, such as a labor-saving device, "technological" seems an appropriate title for these coefficients. Combined with their respective decision variables, the left-hand-side of the constraint in Equation 2.3 represents the use of resources and the right-hand-side represents the availability of resources to be used.

The left-hand-side of the constraints in Equations 2.4 and 2.5 are the same as in Equation 2.3. The right-hand-side of Equation 2.4, though, represents a minimum value for the left-hand-side to equal. This value may, for example, represent the minimum fixed labor hours required to be used in a production plant or some fixed minimum number of calories to be used in a diet. It is alright to exceed b_i in Equation 2.4, but not to solve for the values of x_j where the resulting left-hand-side summation is less than b_i.

In Equation 2.5, we have a strict linear equality side constraint. The left-hand-side values must exactly equal b_i. This is a very binding side constraint since both sides of the constraint must exactly equal one another.

Side constraints are always referred to in the plural because we must have two or more constraints in any linear programming problem formulation. Linear programming models must also have two or more decision variables. In the generalized model, it is stated that a problem can have I side constraints. The side constraint element of the model formulation always begins with the words, "subject to." The side constraints state that the objective function, and, therefore, the selection of the decision variables in the objective function, are subject to some additional limitations or restrictions expressed as linear inequalities and equations. While the objective function must contain all the decision variables, the side constraints need only one or more decision variables. The side constraints allow students the opportunity to include in their linear programming models realistic limitations and restrictions that exist in the desire to maximize profit or minimize cost. It is recommended that students label each side constraint with a word or two to the left of the constraint. This will help reduce confusion when formulating linear programming problems.

■ Non-Negativity Requirement

The non-negativity requirement in the generalized maximization model (and for the minimization model) above can be stated as follows:

$$\text{and} \quad x_j \geq 0 \tag{2.6}$$

This element of the linear programming model formulation states that the resulting values of the decision variables cannot be negative. It is an additional condition on the linear programming model and hence we use "and" to begin the expression. These requirements are implied constraints to be added to the side constraints in the model. They are simply a given or necessary condition for the problem formulation.

The purpose behind the non-negative requirement is quite logical. Decision variables usually represent units of some tangible product or service to be produced. How could anyone produce a negative number of automobiles or of service calls? The non-negativity requirement states clearly that negative solution values are not acceptable.

■ *Model Limitations*

Linear programming can be a very valuable decision-making tool when it is used correctly. Sometimes, students who use linear programming are not aware of the underlying assumptions they are making while modeling a problem situation.

When formulating models, students should always remember that linear programming models require a number of assumptions. If these assumptions are violated in modeling a specific problem situation, then linear programming is not an appropriate modeling process for that problem situation. Thus, underlining assumptions act to limit the applicability of linear programming models. Understanding these assumptions will help us to understand the limitations of modeling linear programming problems. The following assumptions must hold true if linear programming is to be successfully utilized:

■ Additivity

Linear programming problem objective functions are formulated by adding (or subtracting) the product of contribution coefficients times their respective decision variables. This implies that in an objective function, the contribution coefficient of one x_j can be added to the contribution coefficient of another product. In a side constraint, additivity implies that the technological usage of one x_j can be added to a second x_j and both can, in summation, use some acceptable amount of b_i.

In most real-world problem situations, additivity is an acceptable assumption. But in problem situations where a synergistic relationship between two or more decision variables exist, additivity will not hold. To illustrate, consider a finance problem. Suppose a finance manager can invest in two stocks. Stock A will return $10 in dividends on each $100 invested per year and Stock B will return $10 in dividends on each $100 invested per year. But, if both stocks are purchased, Stock B will bring $20 individivends per year. The synergistic relationship between the two types of stock investments used in concert violates the additivity assumption of linear programming by generating more benefit than could be achieved by adding the individual benefits together.

■ Linearity

Linearity is related to the decision variables in the objective function and the side constraints. A linear programming model cannot have a multi-degree polynomial expression or decision variable raised to powers greater than one. Most real-world problems can be structured in a linear relationship. For those problem situations that cannot be expressed linearly, there are other types of solution procedures available.

■ Divisibility

The divisibility assumption implies that the decision variables can take on fractional values. In many problem situations this assumption is quite acceptable. For example, suppose a student wanted to determine the optimal number of hours of labor to use in a production facility using linear programming. The resulting solution might require a fractional number of hours to be used. If, in this problem, a person can be employed for a portion of an hour, there is no problem. But, suppose a contractual agreement exists between management and labor such that scheduling of labor must be on an hourly basis. This would require the student to solve the problem seeking an integer solution (i.e., whole hours of labor). To solve an integer linear programming problem requires a special type of linear programming solution procedure. This procedure is discussed in Section 2.6.

■ Finiteness

This assumption requires the resulting optimal solution values of the decision variables in a problem to be finite. This assumption reflects the realistic decision environment students face in modeling real problems. For example, we cannot produce an infinite number of automobiles or TVs because restrictions, at least in the short run, will limit productivity capability.

■ Data Certainty

The data certainty assumption implies that the information used in formulating a linear programming problem must be known with certainty. This means that all contribution coefficients must be accurate, the technological coefficients must exactly describe the resource utilization of the right-hand-side values, and the right-hand-side values must also be exactly correct. In practice, this assumption is the most difficult to make. The a_{ij}, b_i, and c_j values are rarely all known with certainty. These values are often calculated from subjective input provided by the people who work in the problem situation that is being modeled. Calculations are sometimes forecasted by averaging values or by determining expected values, given some probability estimates. As with forecasting, the longer the time period the estimates for a_{ij}, b_i, and c_j are used, the greater is the chance that the estimates will not be valid. Students should select a relevant time period for planning that is realistic and useful for decision-making. One rule of thumb is, the shorter the time period, the better. The shorter the time period the more likely the values of a_{ij}, b_i, and c_j will remain stable. It is therefore a necessary requirement that a static time period be selected. Over this static time period, the linear programming parameters must remain static. If, on the other hand, a linear programming problem's values are uncertain, there are other solution techniques available to solve this type of problem.

■ 2.3 ■ Formulating the Linear Programming Problem

Before a problem can be solved, it must be defined and stated in an understandable format. Formulating a linear programming problem requires parameter definitions and a model statement. This section presents a formulation procedure to guide students in the formulation of linear programming problems. This section also presents a set of problems that illustrate how linear programming problems can be formulated.

■ *Formulation Procedure*

Each student is exposed to a unique set of learning experiences in life. As such, each student's perception and organization of information is different. These perceptual and organizational differences can cause difficulty in locating and defining the mathematical information needed to formulate a linear programming problem.

The number of parameters that make up the objective function and the side constraints are usually structured in problems in a way that the composition of the linear programming problem can be quite confusing. There is no single right way to formulate a linear programming problem. The following five-step procedure is presented as a guide to students:

1. *Determine the type of linear programming problem:* This step requires students to decide whether the linear programming problem is one of maximization or minimization. Sometimes the type of problem will be clearly stated in the text of the problem. Alternatively, this is accomplished by looking within the problem and finding profit or cost coefficients. If the problem presents profit information, it will usually be a maximization problem. If the problem deals more with cost, it will usually be a minimization problem. Sometimes, contribution coefficients must be derived by the calculation of several values in the problem situation. For example, if sales or gross contribution information is given, see if this information can be matched up with the cost information. If it can, the difference between sales or gross contribution and costs is profit. The problem then becomes a maximization problem.

2. *Define the decision variables:* Clearly state a complete and full definition of the decision variables. In this way, not only the student understands what is being solved for, but also others who utilize the model results will also understand the model's variables. If the decision variables are difficult to determine, remember that each decision variable must have a contribution coefficient. The number of contribution coefficients used to determine the type of problem can be used to help identify the decision variables.

3. *Formulate the objective function:* Since we have already determined the type of linear programming problem and have defined the decision variables, we

31

can combine the information to formulate the objective function. This step is straightforward, and if the decision variables are clearly defined, the objective function can be easily stated.

4. *Formulate the side constraints:* The most difficult part of linear programming problem formulation is to formulate side constraints. This part of the modeling procedure is often considered more of an art than a science. Depending on the way in which the problem information is communicated, there are basically two approaches that can be suggested. The first approach we will call the "right-hand-side" approach. The b_i, right-hand-side values are occasionally listed as maximum available resource quantities in a maximization problem, and minimum usage resource quantities in a minimization problem. Once these maximization or minimization quantities are located, the decision variables related to the right-hand-side values can be matched with their respective technological coefficients. The direction of the inequality sign is based on whether the b_i value is a maximum resource value (i.e., requiring a $\leq$ sign) or a minimum resource value (i.e., requiring a $\geq$ sign).

The second approach to formulating side constraints can be called the "left-hand-side" approach. In some problem situations, the technological coefficients are listed in tables or rows within a word problem. In this type of problem situation it is easier to formulate the left-hand-side of the constraints first. This is accomplished by taking all the values that appear to be technological coefficients and listing them in rows or columns. Remember that the rows in the linear programming formulation should represent technological coefficients that can be attached to different decision variables, while the columns should represent technological coefficients that can be attached to only one type of decision variable. After making up this matrix of numbers, attach the appropriate decision variables to their respective technological coefficients, then identify and attach the appropriate right-hand-side values and add the inequality signs to complete the constraints.

5. *State the non-negativity requirements:* Stating the non-negativity requirements involves setting each of the decision variables, in either type of linear programming problem, greater than or equal to zero. This simply states that we cannot generate negative decision variable values. The expression used in Equation 2.6 is usually what is placed in all linear programming problem formulations.

The five-step formulation procedure presented above is a basic guide to formulating linear programming problems. Students are encouraged to develop their own approaches. To illustrate the linear programming problem formulation procedure, we will now examine a set of problems and their formulation.

■ *Problem Set*

This section contains two linear programming problem situations. Each of the problems are followed by their formulation as a linear programming problem, model parameters definitions, and formulation discussion.

■ Problem 1:

The Texas Tool Company manufactures two special medical surgery instruments, A and B. The owner of Texas Tool would like to determine the weekly production rate in units for the two instruments. The weekly raw material availability for instrument A limits production to 250 units or less. The weekly raw material availability for instrument B limits production to 200 units or less. Due to a fixed investment in raw material for instrument B, at least 100 units must be produced. The maximum number of labor hours available to produce both types of instruments is 175 per week. It takes ½ hour of labor to produce either type of instrument. The unit profit for instrument A is $30 and $35 for B.

■ Formulation

Maximize: $Z = 30x_1 + 35x_2$

subject to:

$$x_1 \leqslant 250 \quad \text{(maximum material A)}$$
$$x_2 \leqslant 200 \quad \text{(maximum material B)}$$
$$x_2 \geqslant 100 \quad \text{(minimum material B)}$$
$$\tfrac{1}{2}x_1 + \tfrac{1}{2}x_2 \leqslant 175 \quad \text{(labor hours)}$$

and $x_j \geqslant 0$

where

x_1 = number of units of instrument A to produce per week

x_2 = number of units of instrument B to produce per week

Since the Texas Tool problem presents only profit information, it is a maximization type linear programming problem. We will use an objective function similar in form to Equation 2.1. The decision variables are clearly stated in units of product and by time. The contribution coefficients of $30 and $35 are placed, with their respective decision variables, together in the objective function. The first, second, and fourth side constraints are similar in form to Equation 2.3. The right-hand-side values of these constraints all represent maximum values in which the left-hand-side of the constraints must be less-than or equal-to. The third constraint in the linear programming formulation has a minimum value whose left-hand-side must be greater than or equal to the b_i value. This side constraint is similar in form to Equation 2.4. Note that all of the constraints are labeled with a few words. This labeling helps to identify the purpose of the side constraint and can also help students to keep track of what constraints have been modeled. Finally, the non-negativity requirement completes the formulation.

■ Problem 2:

Three students, A, B, and C, work in Mary Jane's Drug Store during the school year. Mary Jane needs exactly 40 hours of student labor each week. The number of hours each of the three students work in the drug store is limited. Student A

33

must work 20 hours or more each week. Student B can work only 15 hours per week or less. Student C must work more-than or equal-to the difference in hours between student A and B. Each of the three students hourly wages are $2.50, $1.50 and $3.00, respectively. Mary Jane also contributes an additional $.50 per hour as a hospitalization benefit. What is the minimum cost assignment of working hours for the three students?

■ Formulation

$$\text{Minimize:} \quad Z = 3x_1 + 2x_2 + \tfrac{1}{2}x_3$$

$$
\begin{aligned}
\text{subject to:} \quad & x_1 + x_2 + x_3 = 40 && \text{(total hours)} \\
& x_1 \geqslant 20 && \text{(minimum A hours)} \\
& x_2 \leqslant 15 && \text{(maximum B hours)} \\
& -x_1 + x_2 + x_3 \geqslant 0 && \text{(C hours required)} \\
\text{and} \quad & x_j \geqslant 0
\end{aligned}
$$

where:

x_1 = number of hours student A should be assigned weekly
x_2 = number of hours student B should be assigned weekly
x_3 = number of hours student C should be assigned weekly

Since the Mary Jane's Drug Store problem presents only cost information it is a minimization type linear programming problem. We will use an objective function similar in form to Equation 2.2. The decision variables are clearly stated in hours of labor to be assigned on a weekly basis. The contribution coefficients in this formulation had to be calculated by adding $.50 to each student's wage costs. The first side constraint is an example of a strict linear equality constraint. This is similar in form to Equation 2.5. The third side constraint is similar in form to Equation 2.3. The second and fourth side constraints are similar in form to Equation 2.4. The fourth constraint required some additional calculations. In the problem, student C's assigned hours must be greater-than or equal-to the difference in hours between students A and B. Literally expressed, this can be stated as follows:

$$x_3 \geqslant x_1 - x_2$$

But side constraints must have known constant values on their right-hand-side and all the unknown variables on their left-hand-side. To accomplish this in the fourth constraint, we simply subtract x_1 from both sides of the constraint and add x_2 to both sides of the constraint. This arithmetic adjustment to the mathematical expression above does not alter the restrictive property of the constraint or invalidate the side constraint in any way. Finally, the non-negativity requirements are added to complete the linear programming problem formulation.

Having seen how to formulate linear programming problems, the next step is to see how to *solve* these problems. Section 2.4 presents procedures for solving linear programming problems.

■ 2.4. ■ Linear Programming Solution Procedures

Solution procedures for solving formulated linear programming problems date back to 1947 when G.B. Dantzig first presented his simplex solution method.[1] Modifications to the linear programming simplex method were later made by others, such as W.J. Baumol[2] and N.K. Kwak.[3] These later modified solution methods reduce computational effort considerably when compared to the original Dantzig method. The linear programming solution procedure presented in this section is based on these later modified simplex methods.

Since a linear programming problem can be either maximization or minimization, two respective solution procedures are necessary. A maximization solution procedure and a minimization solution procedure are presented in this section. Their use is also illustrated in this section.

■ *Maximization Solution Procedure*

The computational process used to solve a maximization linear programming problem requires a procedure that is used just for maximization problems. The modified simplex procedure for solving a maximization problem can be divided into two general steps: *developing the initial simplex tableau* and *improving the simplex tableau. Tableau* refers to a reformulation of the linear programming problem into a matrix of elements. *Developing the initial simplex* tableau is only performed once during the solution procedure. It involves the restructuring of the linear programming problem formulation into the first tableau. *Improving the simple tableau* involves repeated computations using the modified simplex algorithm to arrive at an optimal solution. Before the procedure for completing these two steps of the solution method is presented, it is necessary to explain how the modified simplex method operates. How the simplex procedure arrives at an optimal solution is best explained using a graph of a linear programming problem. In Figure 2.1, a graph of the constraints to the following sample linear programming problem are presented:

1. Dantzig, G.B., *Linear Programming and Extensions,* Princeton University Press, Princeton: New Jersey, 1963.
2. Baumol, W.J., *Economic Theory and Operations Analysis,* 2nd ed., Prentice-Hall, Inc., Englewood Cliffs, New Jersey, 1965.
3. Kwak, N.K., *Mathematical Programming with Business Applications,* McGraw-Hill Book Company, New York, 1973.

$$\begin{aligned}\text{Maximize:} \quad & Z = x_1 + x_2 \\ \text{subject to:} \quad & 2x_1 + x_2 \leq 8 \\ & x_1 + 3x_2 \leq 9 \\ \text{and} \quad & x_j \geq 0\end{aligned}$$

The side constraints had to be expressed as equalities to be graphed as lines. Since the actual constraints are inequalities, the areas under each line represent a set of values for x_1 and x_2 that satisfy each respective constraint. The area within the line segments, $\overline{AB}$, $\overline{BC}$, $\overline{CD}$ and $\overline{DA}$, represent a set of values that satisfy both side constraints simultaneously. This set of points is referred to as an *area of feasible solutions* for the entire linear programming problem. In all linear programming problems, the optimal solution occurs at one or more corner points labeled A, B, C, or D on the area of feasible solutions (or along a line segment when multiple solutions exist). If all the corner points of the area of feasible solutions were known,

Figure 2.1   Graph of Sample Problem Constraints

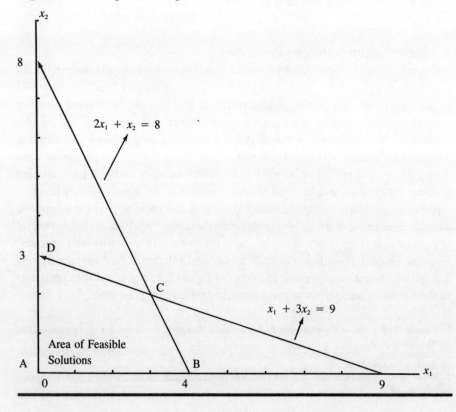

we could use substitution to find the optimal values for the decision variables. We would simply plug each of the corner point values for the decision variables into the objective function to solve for the combination of x_1 and x_2 that generates the largest Z value. In this problem, point A generates a Z of 0, point B results in a Z = 4, point C results in a Z = 5, and point D results in a Z = 3.

What the modified simplex method does is to start from a solution where x_1 and x_2 are equal to zero (i.e., point A in Figure 2.1) and move algebraically from corner point to corner point, eventually to the optimal solution point. Each move from a corner point to another corner point is called an *iteration*. When the optimal solution point is achieved, the simplex method signals a further iteration is not required.

To use the modified simplex procedure requires the previously mentioned steps of developing the initial simplex tableau and improving the simplex tableau.

■ Developing the Initial Simplex Tableau

To illustrate this step of the solution procedure, let us use a generalized linear programming problem:

$$\text{Maximize:} \quad Z = c_1x_1 + c_2x_2$$
$$\text{subject to:} \quad a_{11}x_1 + a_{12}x_2 \leq b_1$$
$$a_{21}x_1 + a_{22}x_2 \geq b_2$$
$$\text{and} \quad x_j \geq 0$$

To develop the initial simplex tableau we must introduce a new type of variable, a *slack variable*. This allows inequalities to be converted into equations. Suppose we take the first constraint of the generalized model above:

$$a_{11}x_1 + a_{12}x_2 \leq b_1$$

By adding the slack variable, s_1, to the left-hand-side of the constraint, we can change the inequality to an equality:

$$a_{11}x_1 + a_{12}x_2 + s_1 = b_1$$

The s_1 variable exists to take up the slack of the difference between $a_{11}x_1 + a_{12}x_2$ and b_1. This is more clearly seen when we express the constraint in terms of a slack variable:

$$s_1 = b_1 - a_{11}x_1 - a_{12}x_2$$

The value of the slack variables may be zero if $b_1 = a_{11}x_1 + a_{12}x_2$, or it may take on a positive value. But the slack variable can never take on a negative value. This would imply the existence of a negative resource.

To proceed with developing the initial simplex tableau, we must reformulate each of the side constraints in terms of their respective slack variables. Since each

37

constraint has its own slack variable, we can add an s_2 variable to the second side constraint. This time, the s_2 is added to the right-hand-side of the constraint:

$$a_{21}x_1 + a_{22}x_2 = b_2 + s_2$$

This expression can then be restructured in terms of its slack variable as follows:

$$s_2 = -b_2 + a_{21}x_1 + a_{22}x_2$$

We must also bring the objective function into the first tableau. The simplex solution procedure requires the initial solution to set all x_j variables equal to zero. If we graphed the problem as we did earlier, the initial solution of all x_j equalling zero means that the initial solution begins at the origin. The mathematical implication is that the slack variables are equal to their respective b_i values. The pragmatic implication is that all available resources have been made idle. This also means that Z must equal zero since:

$$0 = c_1(0) + c_2(0)$$

We can now bring all of these expressions together into the first simplex tableau. In Figure 2.2, a generalized simplex tableau configuration is presented. The tableau is bordered on the top by the term "Non-Basic Variables" and below a listing of the J decision variables that exist in the problem. The x_j decision variables label the columns where the c_j contribution coefficients and a_{ij} technological coefficients are included in the tableau. The left side of the tableau is used to label the rows. The term "Basis" labels the column of s_i slack variables that exist in the initial solution. The "Z" value always equals zero in the initial solution and labels the objective function row whose c_j values follow. The remaining s_i rows label the constraints. Since each constraint has a slack variable, each of the I rows will be labeled with its respective slack variable. The non-negativity requirements, however, are not included in the simplex tableau. The non-negativity requirement is automatically observed mathematically in the modified simplex method.

The generalized maximization problem we have been examining has been placed in a tableau in Figure 2.3. The positioning of these elements in the simplex tableau

---

Figure 2.2   Generalized Simplex Tableau Configuration

		Non-Basic Variables
		x_j
Basis	Z	c_j
s_i	b_i	a_{ij}

Figure 2.3 Initial Tableau for Generalized Maximization Problem

		Non-Basic Variables	
		x_1	x_2
Basis	0	c_1	c_2
s_1	b_1	$-a_{11}$	$-a_{12}$
s_2	$-b_2$	a_{21}	a_{22}

also has informational value. In the Basis column and under the Z value of zero in the initial tableau in Figure 2.3, the resulting optimal solution for the problem will eventually appear. The optimal solution variables, referred to as *solution basis,* will contain the set of decision and/or slack variables that provide the greatest value of Z. The optimized value for Z will also appear where the zero value of Z currently exists. As stated, the initial simplex tableau in Figure 2.3 informs us that $s_1 = b_1$, $s_2 = -b_2$ and $Z = 0$. The variables not in the solution are automatically set equal to zero. These variables are called *non-basic variables* or *zero variables.* This solution is referred to as a *basic feasible solution.* It is *basic* because the variables are in the solution basis, and it is *feasible* because the variables fall within the area of feasible solutions that satisfy all of the problem's constraints. Remember that the origin is one of the corner points on the area of feasible solutions. In each simplex tableau solution, which represents a corner point of the feasible region, the number of basic variables always equals the number of side constraints, and the number of non-basic variables always equals the number of decision variables in the problem. The informational value of the c_j tableau row elements in Figure 2.3 are useful to determine if we have an optimal solution. In an initial tableau we usually do not have an optimal solution. As long as there are positive values in Z row under the variables, we do not have an optimal solution. If we do not have an optimal solution, we must revise the simplex tableau to improve the solution.

■ Improving the Simplex Tableau

Improving the simplex tableau requires a series of continuous revisions in the initial tableau until we arrive at the optimal solution. These revisions take the form of moving variables into and out of the solution basis until the optimal solution set of variables are determined. To improve the initial simplex tableau, use the following steps:

1. *Select the pivot column:* In selecting the pivot column, we are actually selecting the variable that will go into the solution basis. We call this a *pivot* column

because we use the elements in this column to calculate the new elements in the next tableau. The calculation of the new elements involves a repeated use or a pivoting back to these column elements.

The pivot column is selected from those columns labeled non-basic variables. In Figure 2.3 we have two decision variables that are non-basic, x_1 and x_2. The column that has the largest positive c_j contribution coefficient value is the pivot column. We select this variable because it will bring the variable with the largest amount of contribution into the solution basis.

2. *Select the pivot row:* The selection of the pivot row determines the variable to exit the solution basis. To determine the pivot row we must take only the *negative* a_{ij} technological coefficients in the pivot column and divide them into their respective b_i right-hand-side values. We then change the resulting sign, and the smallest ratio determines the pivot row. The negative elements appearing in the pivot column are only considered because they indicate the amount by which the slack variables would decrease for each unit increase in the incoming x_j decision variable. The smallest ratio row is chosen because we have to satisfy all the side constraints. In effect, we have selected a side constraint (i.e., pivot row) that is more binding than the others, relative to the technological coefficients usage rates in the pivot column. By considering this constraint early in the solution process, we will more fully utilize its available resources and thus maximize Z. The negative element common to both the pivot column and the pivot row is called the *pivot element*.

3. *Formulate the new tableau's framework:* This step involves the structuring of a new tableau framework. In addition to drawing the framework, we must exchange the exiting variable (i.e., basic pivot row variable) with the entering variable (i.e., non-basic pivot column variable). All other variables remain in their same position in the tableau framework.

4. *Calculate the new tableau's elements:* In order to calculate the new tableau's elements, we must utilize the pivot row and the pivot column. At the intersection of the pivot row and pivot column is an element which we call the pivot element. This is used in the calculation of all the new tableau's elements. To accomplish this, we first find the element in the new tableau that corresponds to the old pivot element. We then take the *reciprocal* of the old pivot element. Second, we find the elements in the new tableau that correspond to the old pivot row elements, divide the old pivot row elements by the pivot element, and change the resulting signs. Third, we find the elements in the new tableau that correspond to the old pivot column elements. We then divide the old pivot column elements by the pivot element. Finally, we calculate the remaining elements in the tableau using the following formula:

$$\text{New element} = \frac{\text{Corresponding}}{\text{old element}} - \left[\frac{\text{Product of two corner elements}}{\text{Pivot element}} \right] \quad (2.7)$$

In this formula the two corner elements that will be multiplied together are obtained from the old pivot row and old pivot column. We find these corner elements by looking in the same row and column as the new element that we are trying to calculate. Where the new elements' row intersects the old pivot column, determines the pivot column corner element. Where the new elements' column intersects the old pivot row, determines the pivot row corner element. These two corner elements are then multiplied together, divided by the pivot element and then subtracted from the old corresponding element to generate the new element in the new tableau.

5. *Interpret solution and continue to optimal solution:* Having calculated the elements in the new tableau, we must interpret them. We can have two outcomes each time we finish computing a tableau. One outcome is that the tableau elements are not optimal. We know that we do not have an optimal solution so long as the elements in the objective function under the x_j non-basic variables are positive. When we observe this outcome, we must repeat steps 1 to 5 and continue to repeat them until we obtain an optimal solution. Recalculating these tableaus over and over again is why the simplex method is referred to as an *iterative* procedure. Each tableau requires an iteration or a repetition of the solution procedure. In performing the iterations, we move from the origin to other subsequent corner points in the area of feasible solutions until we reach an optimal solution found at one of these corner points.

The second outcome that can occur at any iteration is an optimal solution. When this happens, we may read the solution from the optimal simplex tableau. The variable set for the optimal solution appears under the Basis column. The optimal values for Z and resulting variables in the solution basis are read off the tableau by equating them with values immediately to their right. This completes the simplex solution procedure for a maximization problem.

The next section presents the simplex solution procedures for minimization problems.

■ Minimization Solution Procedure

The modified simplex method for solving minimization linear programming problems is similar to the maximization procedure. The simplex procedure for solving a minimization problem has the same two steps of developing the initial tableau and improving that tableau, as in the maximization procedure.

■ Developing the Initial Simplex Tableau

To illustrate the minimization procedure, let us see the following generalized linear programming problem:

$$\text{Minimize:} \quad Z = c_1x_1 + c_2x_2$$
$$\text{subject to:} \quad a_{11}x_1 + a_{12}x_2 \geqslant b_1$$
$$a_{21}x_1 + a_{22}x_2 \leqslant b_2$$
$$a_{31}x_1 + a_{32}x_2 = b_3$$
$$\text{and} \quad x_j \geqslant 0$$

To develop the initial simplex tableau we make the inequalities into equalities by adding a slack variable to each side constraint. For the first two constraints we use the same approach as with the maximization procedure:

$$a_{11}x_1 + a_{12}x_2 = b_1 + s_1$$
$$a_{21}x_1 + a_{22}x_2 + s_2 = b_2$$

The third constraint is already an equality but the modified simplex procedure requires an initial solution where a slack variable is equal to the right-hand-side value. This requires the creation of an artificial slack variable. In a maximization problem, the slack variable is added on the left-hand-side of the constraint. In the minimization problem we currently face, we add the artificial variable to the right-hand side value as follows.

$$a_{31}x_1 + a_{32}x_2 = b_3 + s_3$$

We then express all of them in terms of their slack variable:

$$s_1 = -b_1 + a_{11}x_1 + a_{12}x_2$$
$$s_2 = b_2 - a_{21}x_1 - a_{22}x_2$$
$$s_3 = -b_3 + a_{31}x_1 + a_{32}x_2$$

The minimization tableau requires an initial solution where the decision variables are equal to zero. This is the same as a maximization problem. The interpretation of the initial solution is not the same. With maximization, we move from a feasible solution at the origin to an optimal solution. With minimization, the origin where we again begin is not feasible. Otherwise, the optimal solution would be at the origin, since $Z = 0$. We move algebraically from an infeasible solution to an optimal and thus feasible solution. With the simplex procedure for minimization we usually do not have a feasible solution until we arrive at an optimal solution. We again set x_1 and x_2 in the generalized minimization problem equal to zero, and thus the value of Z is also zero.

We can now combine the objective functions with the side constraints to state the initial simplex tableau in Figure 2.4. With the exception of the signs on some of the right-hand-side values and technological coefficients, the initial simplex tableau for the minimization problem is the same as the maximization problem.

One change in the tableau concerns the informational positioning of the elements. To determine if we have an optimal solution or not, we now look at the values of

Figure 2.4   Initial Tableau for Generalized Minimization Problem

		Non-Basic Variables	
		x_1	x_2
Basis	0	c_1	c_2
s_1	$-b_1$	a_{11}	a_{12}
s_2	b_2	$-a_{21}$	$-a_{22}$
s_3	$-b_3$	a_{31}	a_{32}

the variables in the solution basis, instead of the objective function row elements as in a maximization problem. If the values of the variables in the solution basis do not possess negative signs, an optimal solution has been found. If we have a negative value in the solution basis, we do not have an optimal solution and must continue to the next tableau. The solution basis, though, is still in the same position as in a maximization problem. The initial solution to our generalized minimization problem can be read off Figure 2.4 as

$$s_1 = -b_1, \ s_2 = b_2, \ s_3 = -b_3 \text{ and } Z = 0$$

Since we cannot have a negative slack variable, we do not have a feasible solution. So we must improve the initial tableau's solution.

■ Improving the Simplex Tableau

Improving the simplex tableau for a minimization problem is the same as improving a maximization tableau. We will make continued revisions in the tableau by moving variables in and out of the solution basis until an optimal solution is found. To do this we will use the following five steps:

1.   *Select the pivot row:* In selecting the pivot row we determine the variable to exit the solution basis. Selection is based on the variable with the greatest negative number in the solution basis.

2.   *Select the pivot column:* In selecting the pivot column we determine the variable to enter the solution basis. The selection of this column is based upon a computation. We must take only the positive technological coefficients in the pivot row and divide them into their respective objective function row contribution coefficients. The ratio that is the smallest determines the pivot column.

3.   *Formulate the new tableau's framework:* This step is the same as with the maximization problem. We again draw the tableau framework and exchange the entering and exiting variables from the solution basis. The other variables remain in their same positions.

43

4. *Calculate the new tableau's elements:* This is exactly the same as for the maximization procedure. The four rules for computing the new elements are the same as listed before.

5. *Interpret solution and continue to optimal solution:* Having calculated the elements in the second tableau, we must determine if the solution is optimal or not. The solution is optimal if the variables in the solution basis have non-negative values. The solution basis will then provide us the optimal solution. If there is one or more negative values in the solution basis variables, we will have to repeat the previously mentioned four steps over again until an optimal solution is reached.

To illustrate the use of these two solution procedures, we will now use them to solve the problems formulated in the problem set of Section 2.3. Students are encouraged to re-read the procedural steps required to solve each type of linear programming problems.

■ Problem Set

■ Application 1

To illustrate the use of the maximization solution procedure for linear programming problems, we will solve the Texas Tool Company Problem presented in Section 2.3. The formulation of this problem is as follows:

$$\text{Maximize:} \quad Z = 30x_1 + 35x_2$$
$$\text{subject to:} \quad x_1 \qquad\qquad \leqslant 250 \quad \text{(maximum material A)}$$
$$x_2 \leqslant 200 \quad \text{(maximum material B)}$$
$$x_2 \geqslant 100 \quad \text{(minimum material B)}$$
$$\tfrac{1}{2}x_1 + \tfrac{1}{2}x_2 \leqslant 175 \quad \text{(labor hours)}$$
$$\text{and} \quad x_j \geqslant 0$$

where:

x_1 = number of units of instruments A to produce per week

x_2 = number of units of instruments B to produce per week

The first step in solving this maximization problem is to place the formulation into an initial tableau. We begin by adding the appropriate slack variables to each constraint as follows:

$$x_1 \qquad\quad + s_1 = 250$$
$$x_2 + s_2 = 200$$
$$x_2 \qquad = 100 + s_3$$
$$\tfrac{1}{2}x_1 + \tfrac{1}{2}x_2 + s_4 = 175$$

We then restructure these equalities in terms of their slack variables as follows:

$$s_1 = 250 - x_1$$
$$s_2 = 200 \qquad - x_2$$
$$s_3 = -100 \qquad + x_2$$
$$s_4 = 175 - \tfrac{1}{2}x_1 - \tfrac{1}{2}x_2$$

These equalities, as well as the objective function's contribution coefficients and the Z value of zero, can be placed in the tableau framework to complete the initial or first tableau as follows:

FIRST TABLEAU

		Non-Basic Variable	
		x_1	x_2
Basis	0	30	35
s_1	250	-1	0
s_2	200	0	$\left(-1\right)$
s_3	-100	0	1
s_4	175	$-\frac{1}{2}$	$-\frac{1}{2}$

Having completed the first tableau, we must now interpret it and determine if we need to improve the existing solution. Currently, the solution is $s_1 = 250$, $s_2 = 200$, $s_3 = -100$, $s_4 = 175$ and $Z = 0$. The values of x_1 and x_2 are zero since they are non-basic variables. This is not an optimal solution because the c_j values (i.e., 30 and 35) are positive. So we must develop the next tableau.

We begin to develop this second tableau by determining the variable to enter the solution basis. Since $35 > 30$, x_2 is the entering variable. This variable also labels the pivot column. We next determine the variable to exit the solution basis. By dividing the negatively signed values in the pivot column into their respective b_i values and changing the resulting sign, we have 200 (i.e., $-200 \div -1$) and 350 (i.e., $-175 \div -\frac{1}{2}$). Since $200 < 350$, s_2 is the exiting variable. This variable also labels the pivot row. The pivot element -1 is at the intersection of the pivot column and pivot row. This element will always be circled.

Having determined the pivot row and pivot column, the entering and exiting variables can be exchanged and the new tableau's framework can be stated. The elements in the new tableau must be calculated using the rules in Section 2.4., "Improving the simplex tableau," step 4. First, the new element that corresponds to the pivot element in the first tableau is its reciprocal. This value is -1 since $1 \div -1 = -1$. Second, the new elements that correspond to the old pivot row elements in the first tableau are found by dividing each element in the pivot row by the pivot element and then changing the resulting signs. These values are 200 and 0, since $-(200 \div -1) = 200$ and $-(0 \div -1) = 0$. Third, the new elements that correspond to the old pivot column elements in the first tableau are found by dividing each element in the pivot column by the pivot element. These values are -35, 0, -1 and ½ since $35 \div -1 = -35$, $0 \div -1 = 0$, $1 \div -1 = -1$ and $-½ \div -1 = ½$. Finally, the remaining elements are calculated using Equation 2.7. For example, the new element that corresponds to the 175 element in the s_4 row in the first tableau is found by:

$$\text{New element} = 175 - \frac{(200 \cdot - ½}{-1}$$
$$= 175 - 100$$
$$= 75$$

For a second example, the new element that corresponds to the -1 element in the s_1 row in the first tableau is found by:

$$\text{New element} = -1 - \frac{(0 \cdot 0)}{-1}$$
$$= -1 + 0$$
$$= -1$$

Below is the second tableau with all the remaining elements included:

SECOND TABLEAU

		Non-Basic Variables	
		x_1	s_2
Basis	7000	30	-35
s_1	250	-1	0
x_2	200	0	-1
s_3	100	0	-1
s_4	75	$-½$	½

We again must interpret this new, second tableau. The solution is $s_1 = 250$, $x_2 = 200$, $s_3 = 100$, $s_4 = 75$ and $Z = 7000$. This solution is better than the first tableau's, since the Z of 7000 is greater than the prior Z value of zero, but it is not optimal. We can see that the solution is not optimal because the objective function value of 30 is still positive. This lack of optimality necessitates a third tableau which is generated using the same iterative procedure again. The resulting third tableau is as follows:

THIRD TABLEAU
Non-Basic Variables

Basis	11500	s_4	s_2
		-60	-5
s_1	100	2	-1
x_2	200	0	-1
s_3	100	0	-1
x_1	150	-2	1

Interpreting this simplex solution we see that $s_1 = 100$, $x_2 = 200$, $s_3 = 100$, $x_1 = 150$ and $Z = 11500$. Since the objective function values of -60 and -5 are both negative, we have an optimal solution. The interpretation of this solution for the tool company is more pragmatic. The Texas Tool Company should produce 150 units of instrument A and 200 units of instrument B per week. The production of these instruments will be at a rate of 100 units of A less than the maximum production rate and 100 units of B more than the minimum production rate. The resulting profit generated will be $11,500.

■ Application 2

To illustrate the use of the minimization solution procedure for linear programming problems, we will solve the Mary Jane's Drug Store Problem presented in Section 2.3. The formulation of the problem is as follows:

$$
\begin{aligned}
\text{Minimize:} \quad & Z = 3x_1 + 2x_2 + \tfrac{7}{2}x_3 \\
\text{subject to:} \quad & x_1 + x_2 + x_3 = 40 && \text{(total hours)} \\
& x_1 \geq 20 && \text{(minimum A hours)} \\
& x_2 \leq 15 && \text{(maximum B hours)} \\
& -x_1 + x_2 + x_3 \geq 0 && \text{(C hours required)} \\
\text{and} \quad & x_j \geq 0
\end{aligned}
$$

where:

x_1 = number of hours student A should be assigned weekly
x_2 = number of hours student B should be assigned weekly
x_3 = number of hours student C should be assigned weekly

The first step to solving this minimization problem is to place the formulation into an initial tableau. We begin by adding the appropriate slack variables to each constraint as follows:

$$x_1 + x_2 + x_3 = 40 + s_1$$
$$x_1 \qquad\qquad = 20 + s_2$$
$$x_2 + s_3 = 15$$
$$-x_1 + x_2 + x_3 = 0 + s_4$$

We then restructure these equalities in terms of their slack variables as follows:

$$s_1 = -40 + x_1 + x_2 + x_3$$
$$s_2 = -20 + x_1$$
$$s_3 = 15 \qquad\quad - x_2$$
$$s_4 = 0 \ - x_1 + x_2 + x_3$$

These equalities, as well as the objective function's contribution coefficients, and the Z value of zero, can be placed in the tableau framework to complete the initial or first tableau as follows:

FIRST TABLEAU

		Non-Basic Variable		
		x_1	x_2	x_3
Basis	0	3	2	½
s_1	-40	1	①	1
s_2	-20	1	0	0
s_3	15	0	-1	0
s_4	0	-1	1	1

Having completed the first tableau we must now interpret it and determine if we need to improve the existing solution. Currently, the solution is $s_1 = 40$, $s_2 = -20$, $s_3 = 15$, $s_4 = 0$ and $Z = 0$. The values of x_1 and x_2 are zero since they are non-basic variables. This is not an optimal solution because the values of -40 and -20 under the Z value are negative. So we must develop the next or second tableau. We begin to develop this second tableau by determining the variable to exit the solution basis. Since -40 is the most negative value in the solution basis, s_1 is the exiting variable. This variable also labels the pivot row. We next determine the variable to enter the solution basis. By dividing the positively signed values in the pivot row into their respective objective function c_j values and changing the resulting sign, we have 3 (i.e., $3 \div 1$), 2 (i.e., $2 \div 1$) and ½ (i.e., $½ \div 1$). Since $2 < 3$ or ½, x_2 is the entering variable. This variable also labels the pivot column. The remaining steps to formulate the second tableau are exactly the same as illustrated in maximization procedure. The resulting second tableau is as follows:

SECOND TABLEAU

		Non-Basic Variables		
		x_1	s_1	x_3
Basis	80	1	2	$\frac{3}{2}$
x_2	40	-1	1	-1
s_2	-20	1	0	0
s_3	-25	①	-1	1
s_4	40	-2	1	0

We again must interpret this new, second tableau. The solution is where $x_2 = 40$, $s_2 = -20$, $s_3 = -25$, $s_4 = 40$ and $Z = 80$. We can see that the solution is not optimal because of the presence of the negative values, -20 and -25 for the basic solution variables s_2 and s_3. A further iteration is necessary. The third and subsequent fourth tableaus are as follows:

THIRD TABLEAU

		Non-Basic Variables		
		s_3	s_1	x_3
Basis	105	1	3	$\frac{1}{2}$
x_2	15	-1	0	0
s_2	5	1	1	-1
x_1	25	1	1	-1
s_4	-10	-2	-1	②

FOURTH TABLEAU

		Non-Basic Variables		
		s_3	s_1	s_4
Basis	107.5	$\frac{3}{2}$	$\frac{7}{2}$	$\frac{1}{4}$
x_2	15	-1	0	0
s_1	0	0	$\frac{1}{2}$	$-\frac{1}{2}$
x_1	20	0	$\frac{1}{2}$	$-\frac{1}{2}$
x_3	5	1	$\frac{1}{2}$	$\frac{1}{2}$

Interpreting the fourth tableau reveals an optimal solution where $x_2 = 15$, $s_1 = 0$, $x_1 = 20$, $x_3 = 5$ and $Z = 107.5$. The interpretation of this solution for the drug store is more pragmatic. Mary Jane's Drug Store should assign student A 20 hours, student B 15 hours and student C 5 hours per week. If they do, they will fully satisfy all of the side constraint requirements and pay only \$107.50 in wages and benefits per week.

The solution procedures presented in this section are not perfect. Occasionally these solution procedures fail to provide a desired optimal solution and can hide useful decision-making information. The next section discusses some modified simplex solution procedure complications.

■ 2.5 ■ Solution Procedure Complications

We can experience many procedural complications that inhibit solutions and useful information from being generated by our linear programming solution procedure. Some of these procedural complications include: alternative optimal solutions, unbounded solutions, infeasible solutions, degeneracy, and negative right-hand-side values.

■ Alternative Optimal Solutions

It is possible to have an alternative optimal solution, that is, an alternative set of decision variables or slack variables that result in the same optimal Z value solution. An alternative optimal solution is present in a linear programming problem if, in the optimal solution basis, we can exchange variables without altering the value of Z. Alternative solutions occur when the contribution coefficient of the objective function is the same as those of any side constraint or the same in ratio of the technological coefficients of any side constraint. The result is that the objective function is parallel to the side constraint, and we have a tie in the pivot column. Graphically, this occurs when the optimal solution is not found at a single corner point in an area of feasible solutions, but in a larger solution set defined by a line segment.

The modified simplex solution procedure generates a single solution. If an alternative solution exists, one or more zero values will appear in the objective function row of the optimal solution. To illustrate, suppose we solve the following linear programming problem:

$$\begin{aligned} \text{Maximize:} \quad & Z = \tfrac{3}{2}x_1 + \tfrac{6}{5}x_2 + \tfrac{6}{5}x_3 \\ \text{subject to:} \quad & x_1 \leq 500 \\ & x_2 + x_3 \leq 900 \\ \text{and} \quad & x_j \geq 0 \end{aligned}$$

The optimal simplex solution for this problem required three tableaus as follows:

FIRST TABLEAU

		Non-Basic Variables		
		x_1	x_2	x_3
Basis	0	$\frac{3}{2}$	$\frac{6}{5}$	$\frac{6}{5}$
s_1	500	$\boxed{-1}$	0	0
s_2	900	0	-1	-1

SECOND TABLEAU

		Non-Basic Variables		
		s_1	x_2	x_3
Basis	750	$-\frac{3}{2}$	$\frac{6}{5}$	$\frac{6}{5}$
x_1	500	-1	0	0
s_2	900	0	$\boxed{-1}$	-1

THIRD TABLEAU

		Non-Basic Variables		
		s_1	s_2	x_3
Basis	1830	$-\frac{3}{2}$	$-\frac{6}{5}$	0
x_1	500	-1	0	0
x_2	900	0	-1	1

The optimal solution is where $x_1 = 500$, $x_2 = 900$ and $Z = 1830$. But an alternative solution exists because of the 0 in the objective function row, under the x_3 non-basic variable. To obtain this alternative solution requires an additional iteration. Note in the second tableau above, either of the non-basic x_2 or x_3 variables could have been chosen for the pivot column. We arbitrarily selected x_2. To determine an alternative solution, we must start with the second tableau and pivot off of x_3 to derive a new third tableau. If we do this, the following "new" third tableau is generated:

		Non-Basic Variables		
		s_1	x_2	s_2
Basis	1830	$-\frac{3}{2}$	0	$-\frac{6}{5}$
x_1	500	-1	0	0
x_3	900	0	1	-1

The alternative solution is where $x_1 = 500$, $x_3 = 900$ and $Z = 1830$. The Z value has remained the same but the decision variables in the solution basis have changed. In reality, there may be many more alternative solutions than can be found using the modified simplex method. The simplex method only provides the values at the corner points of what may be an optimal line segment on the edge of an area of feasible solutions.

■ Unbounded Solutions

An unbounded solution is not a solution; instead, its presence indicates the problem is unsolvable as formulated. An unbounded solution occurs when the area of feasible solutions has borders that would permit the decision variables to take on infinite values. Note in Figure 2.5 the graph of the following sample linear programming problem defines an area of feasible solutions that permit infinite values for the decision variables:

$$\text{Maximize:} \quad Z = 8x_1 + 5x_2$$
$$\text{subject to:} \quad x_1 - 3x_2 \leq 10$$
$$-x_1 + 2x_2 \leq 20$$
$$\text{and} \quad x_j \geq 0$$

The modified simplex solution procedure informs students that the problem they are trying to solve has an unbounded solution. To illustrate, suppose we try to solve the sample maximization problem graphed in Figure 2.5. The resulting tableaus would be generated:

FIRST TABLEAU

		Non-Basic Variables	
		x_1	x_2
Basis	0	8	5
s_1	10	$\boxed{-1}$	3
s_2	20	1	-2

SECOND TABLEAU

		Non-Basic Variables	
		s_1	x_2
Basis	80	-8	29
x_1	10	-1	3
s_2	10	-1	1

Figure 2.5 Graph of Sample Unbounded Solution

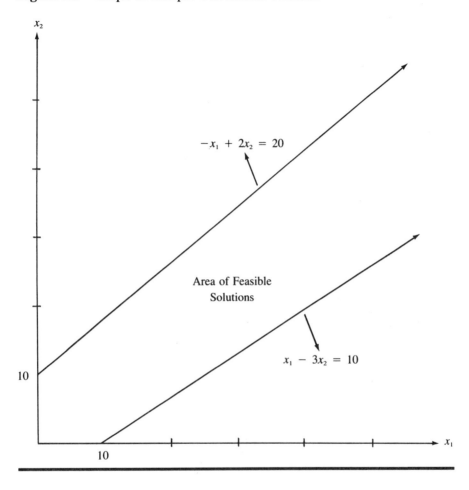

In the second tableau, we do not have an optimal solution and yet we cannot continue to pivot to the next tableau. When we do not have an optimal solution and cannot find a pivotal element that permits the next tableau to be computed, we have an unbounded solution. In this way, the modified simplex method signals students as to the nature of the dilemma they are facing. There is no solution to an unbounded problem. Usually, a problem is unbounded because of a poor formulation. Students are encouraged to review their linear programming problem formulation for formulation errors if an unbounded solution is detected.

53

■ *Infeasible Solutions*

An infeasible solution means that a solution to the problem as formulated does not exist. Infeasibility is caused by poor formulation. To achieve an infeasible solution a student would have to formulate a problem where one or more of the side constraints are violated. The modified simplex solution procedure alerts students to the existence of an infeasible solution. It does this by leaving negativity-signed values in the solution basis. Since all decision and slack variables must be greater-than or equal-to zero, we have an infeasible solution.

■ *Degeneracy*

Degeneracy occurs when we have more than one eligible pivot element in a tableau. It can occur in either a maximization or minimization problem. Degeneracy will not prevent us from obtaining a solution but it can result in needless additional computation. The simplex tableau informs us that we have a degenerate solution by having one of the basic variables in the solution basis equal zero. The Mary Jane's Drug Store problem in Application 2 reveals that it is a degenerate solution.

■ *Negative Right-Hand-Side Values*

The modified simplex procedure cannot solve problems that have negative right-hand-side values. The reason is because the negative right-hand-side value prohibits pivot row selection and generally disrupts pivoting logic. The simple solution to this problem is to multiply the entire side constraint by a -1. This adjustment does not change the resulting solution but does permit the side constraint to be included in the solution process. No readjustment is necessary after an optimal solution is obtained.

The solution complication procedures presented in this section help us solve linear programming problems for x_j values greater than or equal to zero. In the Problem Set presented in Section 2.4, integer variable values resulted, but were not guaranteed by the modified simplex solution procedure presented. If a non-integer solution had resulted, and an integer solution was desirable, a solution-revising procedure would be necessary to derive an integer solution. In Section 2.6, a procedure to derive integer solutions is presented.

■ 2.6 ■ An Integer Linear
Programming Solution
Procedure

There are several integer solution procedures. Some of these methods are called the cutting-plane method, implicit enumeration and the branch-and-bound method. Of these solution procedures, we will use a branch-and-bound method.

■ *Solution Procedure*

Some of the integer linear programming solution methods are used to solve problems that either require the decision variables to have partial or all integer values.

The branch-and-bound method for solving integer linear programming problems can be used where the decision variable values are required to be all integer or where only select variables are required to be integer. The procedure involves the reformulation of linear programming problems and the repeated use of the same modified simplex solution procedure presented in Section 2.4. The integer solution is forced to occur due to the reformulation of the problem, not because of the simplex solution procedure. So what is important in solving for an integer linear programming solution is to know how to adjust the formulation of the problem and to know when an optimal solution has been achieved. To aid in solving integer linear programming problems, the following steps of the branch-and-bound solution procedure are presented for maximization type linear programming problems:

1. Solve the original linear programming problem using the solution procedure presented in Section 2.4. If the resulting solution satisfies the integer problem requirements, stop. If the solution does not satisfy the integer problem requirements, continue to the next step.

2. Select the non-integer decision variable with the largest fraction and develop two side constraints to bind this decision variable. These constraints can be formulated as follows:

$$x_j \le \text{decision variable value rounded down to} \qquad \textbf{(2.8)}$$
$$\text{the next integer value}$$
$$x_j \ge \text{decision variable value rounded up to} \qquad \textbf{(2.9)}$$
$$\text{the next integer value}$$

3. Add the new side constraint from Equation 2.8 to the original linear programming problem and solve this new problem. This is called a branch problem because it branches off the original problem.

4. Add the new goal constraint from Equation 2.9 to the original linear programming problem and solve this second new problem.

5. The solutions to both of the branch problems generated in steps 3 and 4 must be interpreted.

    a. If both result in integer solutions, select the one that provides the greatest Z value. The optimal integer solution to the original problem is thus achieved and no further steps are necessary.

    b. If one branch solution is integer and the other branch solution is a non-integer solution whose Z value is smaller than the integer solution's Z value, the optimal integer solution has been achieved and no further steps are necessary.

c. If one branch solution is integer and the other branch solution is a non-integer solution whose Z value is greater than the integer solution's Z value, continue to step 6. The integer solution is an acceptable candidate for an optimal solution.

d. If both branch solutions are non-integer, continue to step 6.

e. If any branch problem generates an infeasible solution, that branch is at an end and no subsequent problems can be formulated from that branch problem.

6. For each branch solution that is non-integer, repeat steps 2, 3, 4, and 5 using another non-integer decision variable.

7. Continue to repeat step 6 until the necessary integer values for the decision variables are obtained. If multiple integer solutions exist, the overall optimal solution can then be selected from all of the acceptable integer solutions on the basis of the largest Z value.

The branch-and-bound solution procedure for minimization problems is as follows:

1. (Same as maximization procedure.)

2. (Same as maximization procedure.)

3. (Same as maximization procedure.)

4. (Same as maximization procedure.)

5. The solutions to both of the branch problems generated in steps 3 and 4 must be interpreted.

a. If both result in integer solutions, select the one that provides the smallest Z value. The optimal integer solution to the original problem has been achieved and no further steps are necessary.

b. If one branch solution is integer and the other branch solution is a non-integer solution whose Z value is larger than the integer solution's Z value, the optimal integer solution has been achieved.

c. If one branch solution is integer and the other branch solution is a non-integer solution whose Z value is smaller than the integer solution's Z value, continue to step 6. The integer solution is an acceptable candidate for an optimal solution.

d. If both branch solutions are non-integer, continue to step 6.

e. If any branch problem generates an infeasible solution, that branch is at an end and no subsequent problems can be formulated.

6. (Same as maximization procedure.)

7. Continue to repeat step 6 until the necessary integer values for the decision

variables are obtained. If multiple integer solutions exist, the overall optimal solution can then be selected from all of the acceptable integer solutions on the basis of the smallest Z value.

To illustrate the use of these solution procedures, the next section presents an application of the branch-and-bound method in resolving an integer linear programming problem.

■ *Application*

Suppose we have the following integer linear programming maximization problem:

$$\text{Maximize:} \quad Z = 15x_1 + 20x_2$$
$$\text{subject to:} \quad x_1 \qquad \leq \quad 8$$
$$x_2 \leq 12$$
$$\tfrac{9}{5}x_1 + \tfrac{21}{10}x_2 \leq 312$$
$$\text{and} \quad x_j \geq 0 \text{ and all integer}$$

We can see in the formulation that all x_j decision variables must be integer. To begin the branch-and-bound integer solution procedure we solve the original problem using the usual modified simplex solution procedure (i.e., step 1). In Figure 2.6, the original problem's solution (Problem 1) is presented. Since the x_1 decision variable is non-integer, we do not have an "all integer" solution. So we must create two new side constraints (i.e., step 2). In the Problem 2 formulation below, we can see the new side constraint is added (step 3):

$$\text{Maximize:} \quad Z = 15x_1 + 20x_2$$
$$\text{subject to:} \quad x_1 \qquad \leq \quad 8$$
$$x_2 \leq 12$$
$$\tfrac{9}{5}x_1 + \tfrac{21}{10}x_2 \leq 312$$
$$x_1 \qquad \leq \quad 3$$
$$\text{and} \quad x_j \geq 0$$

This problem's solution is also presented in Figure 2.6. Similarly, we formulate Problem 3 as stated below (step 4):

$$\text{Maximize:} \quad Z = 15x_1 + 20x_2$$
$$\text{subject to:} \quad x_1 \qquad \leq \quad 8$$
$$x_2 \leq 12$$
$$\tfrac{9}{5}x_1 + \tfrac{21}{10}x_2 \leq 312$$
$$x_1 \qquad \geq \quad 4$$
$$\text{and} \quad x_j \geq 0$$

This problem's solution is also presented in Figure 2.6. Since branch Problem 2 is

Figure 2.6   Integer Solutions for Branch-and-Bound Problem

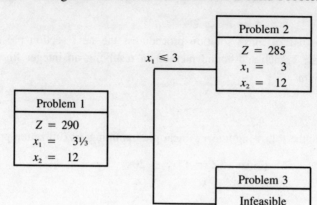

an all integer solution and branch Problem 3 is infeasible, the optimal integer solution is given by Problem 2.

In this section, we have seen how to generate integer solutions for linear programming problems. Some integer problems require their decision variables to be either zero or one in the optimal solution basis. These types of integer problems require a more specialized solution procedure. This specialized solution procedure is called zero-one linear programming.

■ *Zero-One Solutions*

When a linear programming model requires some or all of its decision variables in its optimal solution basis to be either zero or one, we need to use a zero-one linear programming solution procedure. There are several zero-one solution procedures. These procedures include implicit enumeration and branch-and-bound methods.

One of the most common solution approaches for zero-one linear programming problems is the branch-and-bound method. Unfortunately, zero-one problem solutions require a significant amount of computational effort. Even small zero-one problems are very time-consuming when the branch-and-bound solution procedure is used. To reduce the computational requirements in *solving* a zero-one problem, greater care in *formulating* the problem to satisfy the zero-one solution requirements must be given. This may, in some zero-one problems, require the addition of side constraints to the original zero-one problem prior to initiating a branch-and-bound solution procedure. The formulation of these additional goal constraints depends on the problem. That is, we must thoroughly understand the zero-one solution requirements of the problem and use this understanding to generate additional side constraints that will force the zero-one solution we desire. Each problem situation will provide opportunities for insightful students to minimize their computational effort by creating additional side constraints to force a desired zero-one solution with the least number of branching problems. Beyond the addition of these side constraints, we can use the same branch-and-bound procedure presented in Section 2.6. Due to the length of typical zero-one linear programming problems, no problem will be presented here.[4]

■ 2.7 ■ Linear Programming Sensitivity Analysis

Once a linear programming problem is formulated and solved, the information from the solution can be used. Unfortunately, the environment in which the model was abstracted is very dynamic. Changes in profit and cost levels, availability of resources, and the technological usage of those resources are constantly taking place. The solution generated by the modified simplex solution procedure, prior to a change, may no longer be valid. That is, a linear programming problem solution may be very sensitive to a change in one or more of its parameters. One way to examine the sensitivity of a solution to a change in a parameter is to perform a post-solution sensitivity analysis.

There are several types of sensitivity analysis:

1. Changes in c_j values.
2. Changes in b_i values.
3. Changes in a_{ij} values.
4. The adding or subtracting of x_j variables.
5. The adding or subtracting of side constraints.

Each type of sensitivity analysis provides unique information that can save time. The alternative to using sensitivity analysis is simply to effect the change in the linear programming model and observe the result of the change on the solution. With the advent of high-speed computers, many people choose to use this latter approach. But for each type of sensitivity analysis, there are many different types of mathematical solution procedures. These procedures can be used to examine the effect of parameters and model changes with significantly less effort than re-working the problem.[5]

4. For a detailed discussion of zero-one linear programming, see Zionts, S., *Linear and Integer Programming*, Englewood Cliffs, New Jersey, Prentice-Hall, Inc., 1974.
5. For a detailed discussion of sensitivity analysis, see F.S. Hillier and G.J. Lieberman, *Introduction to Operations Research*, 2nd Ed., Holden-Day, Inc., San Francisco, 1974.

■ 2.8 ■ Summary

The subject of linear programming has been presented in this chapter. We have examined the modeling elements that make up a linear programming model. We also reviewed the basic assumptions necessary to understand the limitation on the use of modeling with linear programming. A major portion of this chapter was devoted to the formulation of linear programming problems. The examples provided in the formulation section are designed to expose students to some diversity in the problems they may encounter.

In this chapter, we have also examined the computational procedure for solving linear programming problems using the modified simplex method. Effort was given not only to understand how the simplex procedure worked, but also why it works. The informational value of the simplex method was also presented. Additionally, several common types of simplex computational difficulties were discussed. Their problematic purpose and their resolution were presented.

One of the problem complications encountered in this chapter was infeasible linear programming problems. To resolve these types of unsolvable problems, linear goal programming (LGP) was developed. In the next chapter, we will examine LGP by learning how to formulate LGP problems.

KEY VOCABULARY

Additivity	Left-hand-side values
Algorithm	Linearity
Alternative solution	Maximization problem
Area of feasible solutions	Minimization problem
Artificial slack variable	Modified simplex method
Basic feasible solution	Non-basic variable
Basic variable	Non-negativity requirements
Basis	Objective function
Branch-and-bound method	Parameters
Contribution coefficients	Pivot column
Data certainty	Pivot element
Decision variables	Pivot row
Degeneracy	Right-hand-side values
Divisibility	Sensitivity analysis
Finiteness	Side constraints
Infeasible solution	Slack variable
Iteration	Solution basis

Static time period

Tableau

Technological coefficient

Unbounded solution

Uni-objective

Zero-one programming

Zero variables

Z value

CHAPTER QUESTIONS

2.1 The concept of "finiteness" is both a limitation and an assumption of linear programming. Explain the concept and why it is both.

2.2 Why must there be two solution procedures for linear programming problems?

2.3 How can we tell we have alternative optimal solutions in a linear programming solution?

2.4 Can the branch-and-bound method of solving integer linear programming problems be used to solve zero-one linear programming problems?

2.5 The Getsome Oil Company of Italy produces three types of gasoline: regular, unleaded and superunleaded. Management has decided that it must produce 20,000 gallons of regular, 50,000 gallons of unleaded and 30,000 gallons of super-unleaded in order to meet next week's customer demand. Total production of all gasoline products is 100,000 gallons. The cost of production for a gallon of regular is $.70, unleaded is $.60 and superunleaded is $.67. Formulate this problem as a cost-minimizing linear programming problem.

2.6 The Clarke Production Company manufactures two new pencil products, Zip and Zap. It takes .02 hours of skilled labor and .05 hours of unskilled labor to produce each Zip pencil. It takes .03 hours of skilled labor and .04 hours of unskilled labor to produce each Zap pencil. Each pencil requires 1 ounce of wood, .05 ounce of eraser, 1.6 ounce of lead and .06 ounce of metal. The Zip pencil sells for $.02 and the Zap pencil sells for $.03. The maximum number of skilled hours for the next day is 24, unskilled hours is 36, ounces of wood is 1300, ounces of eraser is 300, ounces of metal is 250 and ounces of lead is 2500. Formulate this problem as a sales-maximizing linear programming problem.

2.7 Lee Products has developed a new dehumidifier system which it plans to market in a few months. The primary channel for the product will be independent distributors. However, the product will also be distributed by a large department store chain and a discount store chain. Because of different distribution and promotional costs, the profit realized by Lee Products varies with the distributor. The table below summarizes pertinent data for the problem.

	Actual Profit Per Unit Sold	Estimated Advertising Cost Per Unit Sold	Estimated Sales Force Effort Per Unit Sold
Independents	$50	$10	2 Hours
Department Store	$40	$8	3 Hours
Discount Store	$30	$15	2 Hours

Lee Products has a weekly advertising budget of $6000 as well as 40 salesmen (at 40 hours per week) available to promote the product. Facilities are such that Lee Products can realize a production capacity of at most 800 units per week. Additionally, contractual arrangements with the discount store require that they receive at least 20% of all units produced. Lee Products wishes to know how to market this product in terms of weekly distribution to each of the distributors. Formulate this problem as a linear programming problem.

2.8 A medical specialist limits her practice to consulting diagnostician. Her expertise is in four service areas which can be labeled A, B, C, and D. She is paid a fixed fee of $500, $600, $800 and $1,000 for each of the four services she provides. Based on past experience, yearly demand for consultations has been estimated to be less than 800, 300, 100 and 40 but more than 200, 150, 75 and 30 for each of the A, B, C, and D services respectively. It takes 3 hours to perform service A, 5 hours to perform service B, 6 hours to perform service C and 10 hours to perform service D. The doctor wants to limit her consultations to no more than 2000 hours per year. The doctor wants to maximize her fee while satisfying her yearly work load requirements. Formulate this problem as a linear programming model.

2.9 The government is interested in determining the optimal number of personnel needed to service the needs of a missile base. A missile base uses three types of personnel: high tech, low tech and administrative. The missile base under study must be able to fire at least 45 heavy nuclear missiles and at least 65 light nuclear missiles in a 10 minute period. It takes 1 high tech, 4 low tech, and 1 administrative personnel to fire one heavy nuclear missile and 1 high tech, 1 low tech, and 1 administrative personnel to fire one light nuclear missile in a 10 minute period. The number of high tech personnel must exactly equal twice the number of low tech personnel. The yearly cost of the personnel amounts to $27,500, $18,500 and $12,500 respectively for high tech, low tech and administrative personnel. Formulate this problem as a linear programming problem.

2.10 The Smith Company manufactures racehorse feed mix from six ingredients: wheat, corn, peanuts, oats, soybeans, and a vitamin supplement. The company produces the feed mix in 1000-pound batches. The cost per pound of each ingredient is as follows:

Ingredient	Cost Per Pound	Minimum Proportion Requirement
Wheat	$.17	10%
Corn	$.04	12
Peanuts	$.26	5
Oats	$.21	10
Soybeans	$.31	5
Vitamins	$.60	20

Every batch that is mixed must satisfy the minimum proportion requirements. These requirements state what percentage of the resulting feed mix batch should be at minimum. Also, the same proportion of wheat and oats must be observed in the final mixture. Formulate this problem as a cost-minimizing linear programming problem.

2.11   Solve the following linear programming problem using the modified simplex solution procedure.

$$\text{Minimize:} \quad Z = 40x_1 + 30x_2$$
$$\text{subject to:} \quad 2x_1 + 4x_2 \geq 16$$
$$3x_1 + 2x_2 \geq 12$$
$$\text{and} \quad x_j \geq 0$$

2.12   Solve the following linear programming problem using the modified simplex solution procedure.

$$\text{Maximize:} \quad Z = 30x_1 + 20x_2$$
$$\text{subject to:} \quad 30x_1 + 20x_2 \leq 180$$
$$20x_1 + 40x_2 \leq 200$$
$$10x_1 \qquad \leq 40$$
$$\text{and} \quad x_j \geq 0$$

2.13   Solve the following linear programming problem using the modified simplex solution procedure.

$$\text{Maximize:} \quad Z = 5x_1 + 2.5x_2$$
$$\text{subject to:} \quad x_1 \qquad = 4$$
$$2x_1 + 8x_2 \leq 40$$
$$x_1 + .5x_2 \geq 5$$
$$\text{and} \quad x_j \geq 0$$

2.14 Solve the following linear programming problem using the modified simplex solution procedure. If there are alternative optimal solutions, determine each.

$$\text{Maximize:} \quad Z = 80x_1 + 70x_2 + 90x_3$$
$$\text{subject to:} \quad 3x_1 + 2x_2 + 4x_3 \leq 100$$
$$x_1 + x_2 + x_3 \leq 40$$
$$2x_1 + 3x_2 + 2x_3 \leq 120$$
$$4x_1 + 3x_2 + x_3 \leq 160$$
$$\text{and} \quad x_j \geq 0$$

2.15 Solve the following linear programming problem using the modified simplex solution procedure.

$$\text{Maximize:} \quad Z = 20x_1 + 8x_2 + 40x_3 + 32x_4$$
$$\text{subject to:} \quad 2x_1 - 4x_2 + x_3 + 2x_4 \leq 12$$
$$20x_1 - 30x_2 + 10x_3 + 70x_4 \leq 320$$
$$4x_1 + 6x_2 - 2x_3 - 2x_4 \leq 24$$
$$\text{and} \quad x_j \geq 0$$

2.16 Solve the following integer linear programming problem using the branch-and-bound solution procedure.

$$\text{Minimize:} \quad Z = 50x_1 + 50x_2$$
$$\text{subject to:} \quad 10x_1 \geq 20$$
$$3x_1 + 8x_2 \geq 24$$
$$3x_1 + 2x_2 \geq 12$$
$$\text{and} \quad x_j \geq 0 \text{ and all integer}$$

2.17 Three workers, A, B and C, must be assigned to three different jobs, I, II and III. The cost of the worker to do each of the three jobs is as follows:

	Job		
Workers	I	II	III
A	$60	$50	$95
B	$30	$40	$10
C	$25	$40	$60

Each worker can do only one job, that is, there is no job splitting. Formulate this problem as a linear programming model.

2.18 Solve the following linear programming problem using the modified simplex solution procedure.

Minimize: $\quad X = 50x_1 + 6x_2 + 10x_3$

subject to: $\quad x_1 + x_2 + x_3 \leq \quad 10$

$\qquad\qquad\quad -x_2 - x_3 \leq -100$

$\qquad\qquad\qquad x_2 \qquad \geq \quad 12$

and $\qquad x_j \geq 0$

3

Formulation of the Linear Goal Programming Model

■ 3.1 ■ Chapter Overview

This chapter explains how problems can be formulated into an LGP model. Generalized LGP models are presented along with several applications to reinforce the formulation learning experience. A brief discussion on model limitations and on how case problems are analyzed is also presented.

■ 3.2 ■ Generalized LGP Models

All LGP models consist of three components: an objective function, goal constraints and non-negativity requirements. Before examining each of these modeling components, several LGP terms need to be defined.

■ *LGP Terminology*

To fully understand any subject area, students must always acquaint themselves with unique terms and expressions used by people in that field of study. The following are definitions of several commonly used LGP terms and expressions.

Decision Variables: A set of unknowns (i.e., represented in the LGP model as x_j, where $j = 1,2,. . .,J$) we are seeking to determine.

Right-Hand-Side Values: Values that usually express resource values (i.e., represented by b_i) that we seek to overutilize or underutilize.

Goal: The desire to minimize numerical deviation from a stated right-hand-side value in a select goal constraint.

Goal Constraints: A set of constraints that express the relevant resource or right-hand-side goals in the problem situation being modeled.

Preemptive Priority Factors: A ranking system (i.e., represented by P_k, where $k = 1,2,. . .,K$ and K represents the number of goals in the model) that allows goals to be ordinarily structured into the LGP model. The ranking system places the importance of goals in accordance with the following relationship: P_1 (Most Important Goal) $> P_2 >>> P_k$ (Least Important Goal).

Deviational Variables: Variables that express the possibility of negative deviation from a goal constraint right-hand-side value (i.e., represented in the LGP model as d_i^-, where $i = 1,2,. . .,I$ and I is the number of goal constraints in the model) or positive deviation from a right-hand-side value (i.e. represented as d_i^+). These variables are conceptually similar to slack variables in linear programming models.

Differential Weights: Mathematical weights that are expressed as cardinal numbers (i.e., represented as w_{kl} where $k = 1,2,. . .,K; l = 1,2,. . .,L$) and are used to differentiate the l, deviational variables within a single k, priority level.

Satisficing: A concept that implies that LGP seeks a solution that fully satisfies as many goals as possible rather than optimizing a single goal. Where we make reference in the text to an optimal LGP solution, we are really referring to a satisficing solution.

Technological Coefficients: Numerical values (i.e., represented by a_{ij}) that express the per unit usage of the b_i value in the creation of the x_j.

■ Objective Functions

There are three different types of LGP objective functions. They can be expressed as follows:

$$\text{Minimize:} \quad Z = \sum_{i=1}^{I} d_i^- + d_i^+ \tag{3.1}$$

$$\text{Minimize:} \quad Z = \sum_{i=1}^{I} P_k(d_i^- + d_i^+) \quad \text{(for } k = 1,2,. . .,K) \tag{3.2}$$

$$\text{Minimize:} \quad Z = \sum_{i=1}^{I} w_{kl}P_k(d_i^- + d_i^+) \text{ (for } k = 1,2,. . .,K; \tag{3.3}$$

$$l = 1,2,. . .,L)$$

In Equation 3.1, Z is the minimized value of the sum of all negative deviations, d_i^-, and positive deviations, d_i^+, in I goal constraints. This objective function is used when deviational variables in a problem situation are not distinguished by priority or weighting. In effect, this type of problem has the unitary goal of minimizing total deviation from all right-hand-side values. Equation 3.2 expresses an objective function where there can be K goals ranked by P_k priorities. This type of objective function is used in problems where the ranking or ordering of goals is required, but the deviational variables within each priority level are of equal importance in the problem situation. In Equation 3.3, goals are ranked and deviational variables within each priority level are to be differentiated by using the w_{kl} differential weighting.

The objective function that will be used is dependent on the problem situation. If a problem situation does not require an ordering or ranking of goals, then we would use the objective function in Equation 3.1. If the problem requires the ranking of goals, but not deviational variables within goals, we would use the objective function in Equation 3.2. If the problem requires both the ranking of goals and a differentiation of the deviational variables within priorities, then we would use the objective in Equation 3.3.

It is interesting to note that there are no decision variables in the objective function of an LGP model. We still seek, as does a linear programming model, to determine the unknown values of x_j, but will do so indirectly by directly minimizing the positive and negative deviation from the goal constraint's right-hand-side values. Linear programming models seek a direct solution for the x_j values by indirectly minimizing deviations from their right-hand-side values.

■ Goal Constraints

There are six different types of goal constraints. The purpose of each type is determined by its relationship with the objective function. In Table 3.1 each of the six types of goal constraints are presented. We can see in Table 3.1 that each type of goal constraint must have either one or two deviational variables placed in the objective function. It is possible to have strict equality constraints containing no deviational variables. These constraints are the same as linear equality constraints. Students should be familiar with their formulation from prior exposure to linear programming.

Equation 3.4 in Table 3.1 is similar in purpose to a $\leq$ inequality constraint in a maximization linear programming problem. Likewise, Equation 3.5 is similar in purpose to a $\geq$ inequality constraint in a minimization linear programming problem. Equations 3.6, 3.7 and 3.8 all permit deviation in both directions, but Equation 3.8 seeks a desired right-hand-side resource usage equal to b_i. This is similar to an equality linear programming constraint, but not as binding on the solution because positive and negative deviation is possible. If a strict linear equality constraint is necessary in an LGP model formulation, it can be included by placing an "artificial" d_i^+ variable in the linear equality constraint, as in Equation 3.9. (This procedure

Table 3.1 Types of Goal Constraints

Equation Number	Goal Constraint	Deviational Variable in Objective Function	Possible Deviation	Unrestricted Deviation	Desired usage of Right-Hand-Side Value
(3.4)	$a_{ij}x_j + d_i^- = b_i$	d_i^-	Negative	None	equal to b_i
(3.5)	$a_{ij}x_j - d_i^+ = b_i$	d_i^+	Positive	None	equal to b_i
(3.6)	$a_{ij}x_j + d_i^- - d_i^+ = b_i$	d_i^-	Negative and Positive	Positive	b_i or more
(3.7)	$a_{ij}x_j + d_i^- - d_i^+ = b_i$	d_i^+	Negative and Positive	Negative	b_i or less
(3.8)	$a_{ij}x_j + d_i^- - d_i^+ = b_i$	d_i^- and d_i^+	Negative and Positive	None	equal to b_i
(3.9)	$a_{ij}x_j - d_i^+ = b_i$	d_i^+ (artificial)	None	None	exactly b_i

is discussed in Section 4.2. under "Initial Tableau Formulation Procedure.") Equations 3.6 and 3.7 permit positive and negative deviation from their respective right-hand-side values if it is desirable. There is no comparable linear programming constraints to Equations 3.6 and 3.7.

With these six types of LGP constraints, we can model any type of LGP problem situation. The actual formulation of these constraints to model problem situations will be discussed in Section 3.3.

■ *Non-Negativity Requirements*

Just as with linear programming, the LGP model variables must be greater-than or equal-to zero. All LGP models include deviational variables as well as decision variables, so the statement of non-negativity can be expressed as follows:

$$x_j, d_i^-, d_i^+ \geq 0 \qquad \qquad (3.10)$$

Unless otherwise noted, the LGP model variables can be defined as any real number.

■ 3.3 ■ Formulating the LGP Problem

To understand how to formulate an LGP problem, we will now look at a formulation procedure. Later we will apply this procedure to several problem situations.

■ *Formulation Procedure*

Formulating an LGP problem is very similar to formulating a linear programming problem. The defining of the decision variables x_j, the technological coefficients a_{ij}, and the right-hand-side values b_i, are required in both the linear programming and LGP. One suggested procedure to formulating LGP models involves the following six steps:

1. *Define the decision variables:* The key here is to clearly state what the unknown decision variables will represent. The more precise the definition, the easier the rest of the modeling exercise will be.

2. *State the goal constraints:* The key here is to identify the right-hand-side variables first and then determine the appropriate technological coefficients and decision variables to include in the constraint. Also, pay particular attention to the wording that describes what type of deviation is permissible from the right-hand-side values. If deviation is permitted in both directions, place both deviational variables in the constraint. If deviation is permitted in only one direction, place only the appropriate single deviational variable in the constraint.

3. *Determine the preemptive priorities:* The key here is to look for a ranking or ordering of goals in the problem situation. Usually the ranked goals will be an individual's stated preferences. If the problem situation does not have any ranking or ordering of goals, then skip this step and the next in the formulation procedure.

4. *Determine the differential weights:* The key here is look for preferences or rankings within a specific goal level. If none exist, skip this step.

5. *State the objective function:* The key here is first to select the correct deviational variables for inclusion in the objective function. Utilize Table 3.1 to make sure the desired usage of the right-hand-side values are consistent with the problem requirements. Second, attach the appropriate preemptive priorities and differential weights if needed.

6. *State the non-negativity requirements:* This is the formal part of the problem statement and can be usually expressed exactly as Equation 3.10.

This general formulation procedure is one approach that may be helpful in formulating LGP problems. Students are encouraged to improve or change the procedure to suit their own unique needs. To help students understand how to formulate LGP problems, the remainder of this section presents a set of problem situations and their LGP model formulations.

■ *Problem Set*
This section contains three LGP problem situations. Each of the problems are followed by their formulation as an LGP problem, model parameter definitions and an explanation of the formulation.

■ Problem 1:
The Ollie Advertising Company is trying to determine how many radio and television commercial spots they should obtain for a new products promotion. A tentative budget for radio and television commercials is $300,000. Budget additions are possible if justified. The cost of a radio commercial is $1,000 and the cost of a television commercial is $3,000. If the advertising company uses radio at all, they must use a minimum of 50 commercial spots. In deciding how to allocate the budgeted funds, the company researched the promotional impact of the two commercial medias. They found that a single radio commercial generated two sales but a single television commercial generated four sales. The advertising company would like to simultaneously fully utilize the targeted $300,000 budget allocation as exactly as possible, satisfy the minimum radio commercial requirement and maximize the new products sales. Formulate this problem into an LGP model.

■ Formulation:

Minimize: $Z = d_1^- + d_1^+ + d_2^+ + d_3^-$

subject to: $x_1 + 3x_2 + d_1^- - d_1^+ = 300$ (budget allocation)

$x_1 \qquad\qquad\quad - d_2^+ = 50$ (radio requirement)

$2x_1 + 4x_2 + d_3^- \qquad = M$ (sales)

and $x_j, d_i^-, d_i^+ \geqslant 0$

where:

x_1	=	number of radio commercial spots to obtain
x_2	=	number of television commercial spots to obtain
d_1^-	=	number of thousands of dollars under budget allocation
d_1^+	=	number of thousands of dollars over budget allocation
d_2^+	=	number of radio commercial spots over minimum requirement
d_3^-	=	number of new products sales under M
M	=	a very large number, in this example an extremely high level of new product sales that will be caused by the promotion on the radio and television. (This number can be determined by arbitrarily selecting a number of sales that is extremely large relative to the budgetary allowance capacities of the model.)

In this objective function neither priorities nor differentiating weights are required. Hence this type of objective function is expressed in the same form as the generalized model presented in Equation 3.1. The first goal constraint represents the budgetary allocation in the problem situation. (To help students identify the nature of each goal constraint it may be worthwhile to use a couple of words in parentheses to the right of the model to label the purpose of each goal constraint.) The budgetary constraints' technological coefficients and its right-hand-side value was divided by 1000 to simplify the computation. In the resulting solution, we will have to readjust the values of the deviational variables by multiplying d_1^+, d_1^- or d_3^- by 1000. Students are encouraged to use this mathematical adjustment to simplify and reduce needless computational effort. The radio requirement constraint does not possess a negative deviational variable because the 50-radio-spot requirement is an absolute minimum that cannot be violated. So negative deviation from the 50 is not permitted. Similarly, if we select a value for M in the new sales constraint that is very high or achievable, positive deviation will be prohibited. So a positive deviational variable for this constraint is not necessary. If positive deviation is possible, a d_3^+ would have to be included.

■ Problem 2:

The Florance Manufacturing Company produces two products, A and B. The company makes $3 in profit on each item sold and can sell a many products as they manufacture. The targeted production is 10 units for Product A and 15 units for Product B. These targets were based on normal production capacity. Actual production capacity can be increased or decreased from the given targeted production levels. In order to provide some minimum level of work, at least 5 units of Product A must be produced. The future profit target is $120. The owner of the company has the following goals in the order of their importance:

P_1 Minimize the overutilization of the targeted $120 profit level.

P_2 Minimize the underutilization of normal production capacity of both products.

P_3 Minimize the overutilization of normal production capacity of both products.

P_4 Minimize the overutilization of minimum production capacity of Product A.

Formulate this problem into an LGP model.

■ Formulation:

$$\text{Minimize:} \quad Z = P_1 d_1^+ + P_2(d_2^- + d_3^-) + P_3(d_2^+ + d_3^+) + P_4 d_4^+$$

$$
\begin{array}{llll}
\text{subject to:} & 3x_1 + 3x_2 + d_1^- - d_1^+ & = & 120 \quad \text{(profit)} \\
& x_1 \qquad\quad + d_2^- - d_2^+ & = & 10 \quad \text{(normal production A)} \\
& \qquad x_2 + d_3^- - d_3^+ & = & 15 \quad \text{(normal production B)} \\
& x_1 \qquad\qquad\quad - d_4^+ & = & 5 \quad \text{(minimum production A)}
\end{array}
$$

and $x_j, d_i^-, d_i^+ \geqslant 0$

where:

x_1	=	units of Product A to produce
x_2	=	units of Product B to produce
d_1^-	=	dollars under profit target
d_1^+	=	dollars over profit target
d_2^-	=	units of Product A under normal production target
d_2^+	=	units of Product A over normal production target
d_3^-	=	units of Product B under normal production target
d_3^+	=	units of Product B under normal production target
d_4^+	=	units of Product A over minimum production requirement

In this objective function, priorities are required to model the problem but no differentiating weights are necessary. Hence, this type of objective function is expressed in the same form as the generalized model presented in Equation 3.2. The first three goal constraints permit deviation in both directions because the problem statement indicated the right-hand-side values were targets, not exact values to be achieved. In the case of the fourth goal constraint, a lower level for the production in units of Product A was stated with the phrase "at least 5 units of Product A must be produced." So this goal constraint does not permit any negative deviation from the minimum production level of 5 units.

■ Problem 3:

The Swifter Trucking Company has been engaged to truck the weekly production of the Quick Computer Company from the Quick production plants to their distribution centers. The Quick Computer Company has three production plants (A, B and C) and five distribution centers (I, II, III, IV and V). Next week, the forecasted number of trucks required at each of the three production plants are: 6 at Plant A, 12 at Plant B and 12 at Plant C. Since the Quick Computer Company produces only one type of computer, any of the three plants' truckloads of computers can go to any of the five distribution centers for disbursement to their retail outlets. The forecasted demand, in truckloads, at each of the distribution centers are 12 at Center I, 6 at Center II, 4 at Center III, 2 at Center IV and 6 at Center V. The traveling distance in miles between each of the production plants and distribution centers is given below:

Production Plant	Distribution Center				
	I	II	III	IV	V
A	100	275	800	625	175
B	225	200	300	500	675
C	700	600	250	150	450

Cost research indicates the operation is unitarily proportional to distance in miles. So, the cost of transporting the computers is one dollar per mile.

The Swifter Trucking Company has truck service facilities in the same city as Distribution Center II. The convenience of sending trucks (or loads of computers) to this distribution center could save the trucking company 10 percent of their operating costs over trucks sent to the other centers. The trucking company, because of legal matters, should not travel any of the highways between Plant A and Distribution Center II. Swifter should also ship the same number of loads originating from Plant B to Distribution Centers I and III because of union contract requirements.

The Swifter Trucking Company would like to establish an assignment schedule that will state which trucks should be assigned to carry loads between the Quick

Computer Company's production plants and distribution centers. The schedule should make these assignments consistent with the following ordered goals:

P_1 Satisfy the forecasted demand of the number of trucks required at each production plant and distribution center and also give preference to service operation cost minimization.

P_2 Minimize legal shipping problems.

P_3 Minimize union shipping problems.

P_4 Minimize traveling distance.

Formulate this problem into an LGP model.

■ Formulation:

Minimize: $Z = 1.1\, P_1(d_5^- + d_5^+) + P_1(d_1^- + d_1^+ + d_2^- + d_2^+ + d_3^- + d_3^+$
$+ d_4^- + d_4^+ + d_6^- + d_6^+ + d_7^- + d_7^+ + d_8^- + d_8^+)$
$+ P_2\, d_9^+ + P_3\, (d_{10}^- + d_{10}^+) + P_4 d_{11}^+$

subject to:

$$x_1 + x_2 + x_3 + x_4 + x_5 + d_1^- - d_1^+ = 6 \quad \text{(Plant A demand)}$$
$$x_6 + x_7 + x_8 + x_9 + x_{10} + d_2^- - d_2^+ = 12 \quad \text{(Plant B demand)}$$
$$x_{11} + x_{12} + x_{13} + x_{14} + x_{15} + d_3^- - d_3^+ = 12 \quad \text{(Plant C demand)}$$
$$x_1 + x_6 + x_{11} + d_4^- - d_4^+ = 12 \quad \text{(Dist. Ctr. I demand)}$$
$$x_2 + x_7 + x_{12} + d_5^- - d_5^+ = 6 \quad \text{(Dist. Ctr. II demand)}$$
$$x_3 + x_8 + x_{13} + d_6^- - d_6^+ = 4 \quad \text{(Dist. Ctr. III demand)}$$
$$x_4 + x_9 + x_{14} + d_7^- - d_7^+ = 2 \quad \text{(Dist. Ctr. IV demand)}$$
$$x_5 + x_{10} + x_{15} + d_8^- - d_8^+ = 6 \quad \text{(Dist. Ctr. V demand)}$$
$$x_2 - d_9^+ = 0 \quad \text{(legal requirement)}$$
$$x_6 - x_8 + d_{10}^- - d_{10}^+ = 0 \quad \text{(union requirement)}$$
$$100x_1 + 275x_2 + 800x_3 + 625x_4 + 175x_5$$
$$+ 225x_6 + 200x_7 + 300x_8 + 500x_9 + 675x_{10}$$
$$+ 700x_{11} + 600x_{12} + 250x_{13} + 150x_{14} + 450x_{15} - d_{11}^+ = 0$$
$$\text{(traveling distance)}$$

and $x_j, d_i^-, d_i^+ \geq 0$

where:

x_j = ($j = 1,2,\ldots,15$) number of trucks to be scheduled between each of the combinations of production plant and distribution center assignments.

d_i^- = ($i = 1,2,\ldots,8$) number of trucks under the demand level required at each of the three production plants and five distribution centers, respectively.

d_i^+ = $(i = 1,2,\ldots,8)$ number of trucks over the demand level required at each of the three production plants and five distribution centers, respectively.

d_9^+ = number of trucks illegally using highways.

d_{10}^- = additional number of trucks used between production plant B and Distribution Center III, over stated union contracted requirements.

d_{10}^+ = additional number of trucks used between Production Plant B and Distribution Center I, over stated union contracted requirements.

d_{11}^+ = total number of miles necessary to be traveled in order to satisfy total truck demand requirements.

In this objective function both priorities and a differential weight are required. The differential weight is based on the 10 percent decrease in cost of operation statement in the problem. Since distance in miles is also the unitary cost of operation, the allocation of the 7 trucks to Distribution Center II is $\frac{1}{10}$ more important than the allocation of trucks to all other production plants and distribution centers. Hence this type of objective function is expressed in the same form as the generalized model presented in Equation 3.3. The first eight goal constraints permit deviation from their respective right-hand-side values because the values were forecasted and possible deviation from the true demand can result. The right-hand-side value of zero in the ninth, tenth and eleventh goal constraints were required to force x_2 to become zero, to equalize x_6 and x_8 and to seek a solution that minimizes traveling distance for all the x_j. These three constraints illustrate one way to model their respective desired goals. There are alternative ways to model these same goals. Students are encouraged to determine these alternative goal constraints.

■ 3.4 ■ LGP Model Limitations

When formulating models, students should always remember that LGP models require a number of assumptions. If these assumptions cannot be made in modeling a specific problem situation, then LGP is not an appropriate modeling process for that situation. Thus, model assumptions act to limit the applicability of LGP. Understanding these assumptions will help us to understand the limitations on the LGP modeling process. The following assumptions must hold true if LGP is to be successfully utilized:

1. *Additivity and Linearity:* It is assumed that proportional usage of b_i defined by a_{ij} must remain true regardless of the resulting solution values x_j. That is, the left-hand-side of a goal constraint must equal the right-hand-side value. This limitation also applies to the objective function. In real-world settings, synergistic

relationships can cause this assumption to be violated. A typical example is where individuals, placed in a competitive environment, are more productive than when an individual's performance is measured in a non-competitive environment. Other modeling procedures, such as stochastic LGP, are available to model these types of problem situations.

2. *Divisibility:* It is assumed that the resulting values for x_j, d_i^- and d_i^+ can be fractional. That is, we can solve for fractional amounts of x_j and use fractional amounts of resources in the solution. This assumption does not limit the use of the LGP model because other LGP solution procedures, such as integer LGP, exist to allow integer solutions to be found.

3. *Finiteness:* It is assumed that the resulting values for x_j, and d_i^-, d_i^+ must be finite. That is, we cannot have unlimited decision variable values, resources or goal deviations. Everything in this world is finite, so the key is in defining the time period for the model.

4. *Data Certainty and Static Time Period:* It is assumed that the LGP model parameters a_{ij}, b_i, P_k and w_{kl} are known with certainty and that they will remain static over a planning period in which the model's results are to be utilized. Few systems in the world are static, but by carefully defining a discrete period of time, model parameters can be known with certainty and be static for useful application in the model.

■ 3.5 ■ Formulating a Case Problem

How a case is formulated is of course dependent on the type of problem observed in the case. Each case in Part II consists of a case, a set of questions and a set of references from which the case was in part developed. The cases in this book have been developed to provide a learning exercise in problem formulation, problem solution and post-solution analysis. With these educational objectives in mind the following steps are recommended as an approach to analyze the cases in Part II of this book:

1. *Preview the case:* Briefly read (or skim) the case and the questions that follow each case. Try to get a perspective on the type of exercise (i.e. problem formulation, problem solution and/or post solution analysis) required by the case problem situation.

2. *Read one or more of the selection references:* Since the case was partially based on the selected references, they will be helpful in understanding the case. Review one or more of them and also select other references from the bibliography in the appropriate application area (e.g. accounting, finance, etc.).

3. *Read the case:* While reading the case, take notes if need be to help pull relevant information together. Identify the major exercise (i.e. educational objective of the case) and any other subsequent analysis being required. Some cases may require several steps and each should be identified and defined.

4. *Perform analysis:* Unless otherwise instructed, the questions at the end of the case define what analysis needs to be completed.

5. *Test the solution:* Basically this involves a common sense approach to determining if the case questions have been answered completely and that the solution "makes sense" in terms of the problem situation. For a problem formulation type exercise the key is to determine if all of the relevant data in the case has been incorporated into the model. It may be helpful to review the case again and check off the model parameters as they appear in the case to insure everything has been considered. For problem solution and post-solution analysis type exercises it may be possible to check the sensibility of the solution by reviewing model goal constraints to see if the problem situation has been violated.

6. *Present the solution:* This step depends on the instructor, but usually a complete case analysis presentation will include a written or oral report consisting of: (1) a brief overview of case background information, (2) a concise statement of the problem requiring a solution, (3) an analysis of the problem, and (4) a set of recommendations that can be implemented.

Formulating a case problem is as much an "art" as it is a "science." Students are encouraged to develop their own approach to the case problems in Part II. Always remember, the type of *approach* used to analyze a case is not as important as the *results* of the analysis. As a rule of thumb, business and industry reward results, not approaches.

■ 3.6 ■ Summary

This chapter has introduced the generalized LGP model and explained how LGP problems can be formulated. The sample problem formulations were designed to help orient the student in the practice of LGP model formulation. This chapter also discussed the necessary assumptions that define the applicability and limitations of LGP modeling.

As can be seen in the bibliography in Section 1.3, there are many different types of problem situations. The formulation process described in this chapter can be applied to any type of LGP problem. Students should review some of the prior research studies to gain a greater understanding of the LGP formulation process.

Problem formulation is only part of any solution process. Having formulated a problem, it must be solved to derive useful decision-making information. In Chapter 4 an LGP solution procedure is presented.

KEY VOCABULARY

Additivity	Goal constraint
Data certainty	Linearity
Decision variable	Non-negativity requirements
Deviational variable	Preemptive priority factors
Differential weights	Right-hand-side values
Divisibility	Satisficing
Finiteness	Static time period
Goal	Technological coefficients

CHAPTER QUESTIONS

3.1   Explain in your own words what the non-negativity requirements are in an LGP problem formulation. Why do we need them?

3.2   How are a goal and goal constraint the same? Cite examples.

3.3   How are a preemptive priority and a goal different? Cite examples.

3.4   In a real-world setting, where do you obtain information for differential weights and why are they necessary in an LGP model?

3.5   Is "divisibility" always necessary in an LGP model? Why?

3.6   Cite examples where "data certainty" can and cannot be assumed in a_{ij} and b_i parameters.

3.7   A stonecutter carves tombstones from granite and limestone blocks. The stonecutter has 5 granite and 5 limestone blocks on stock and may obtain more granite blocks during any week. The stonecutter must use at least her current inventory of five granite blocks and can use no more than five limestone blocks in meeting next week's demand. The maximum number of tombstones she can carve in a week is eight. She would like to determine how many granite and limestone tombstones to carve next week given the following goals in their order of importance:

1.   Fully utilize stonecutter labor.
2.   Minimize granite stones cut.
3.   Maximize limestones cut.

Formulate this problem using LGP.

3.8   A local trucking firm must transport 900, 800, 700 and 1000 units of a product to four cities, A, B, C, and D. The product is manufactured and supplied in two other cities, X and Y, at 1900 and 1500 units respectively. The cost per unit to transport the product between the manufacturing plants in cities X and Y and the demand market cities A, B, C, and D are given below:

Supply	Demand Market			
Plant	A	B	C	D
X	.65	.70	.80	.90
Y	.50	.60	.80	.70

The local trucking firm would like to accomplish the following goals:

1. Satisfy all demand and supply requirements.

2. Prohibit the transport of products between supply Plant X and demand Market A.

3. Minimize transportation costs.

Formulate this problem using LGP.

3.9   A jewelry manufacture makes three different products requiring three different types of materials:

	Units of		
Item	Diamonds	Silver	Gold
Ring	2	10	60
Necklace	1	50	30
Pin	1	30	80

The cost to manufacture a ring is $1000, a necklace $500 and a pin $700. Because of shifting costs of each type of material, the manufacturer would like to alter the company manufacturing policy to underutilize the 40 diamonds available, overutilize the 1500 units of silver available, and underutilize the 2400 units of gold available. Finally, the manufacturer would like to spend $120,000 or less for a budgeted allocation for manufacturing. Formulate this problem using LGP.

3.10   You have been hired as manager of a new pizza place, and your first duty is to hire your staff. Past experience has shown that you will need at least 10 cooks and 15 waitresses. The cooks are three times as time-consuming to manage as are the waitresses. The restaurant is large enough to house about 30 employees at a time. Managers can adequately supervise 40 employees at a time. The starting salary for cooks is $400/month and the salary for waitresses is $600/month. The tentative monthly budget is $17,000. Your goals include:

1. adequate minimum customer service,

2. adequate supervision for employees,

3. minimum utilization of physical resources, and

4.   fully utilizing payroll budget.

Formulate as an LGP model.

3.11   The Kodo factory is producing two basic types of cameras for a sales promotion. They are the Instamatic III and the Kodo Super XX (35 mm). From recent production of the two, Kodo has found that both cameras require the same average of five hours of production time. The production capacity usually runs about 160 hours for two weeks. Kodo estimates the sales for the Instamatic III to be 50 a week. The estimated sales for the 35 mm camera are 75 a week. They are expecting high sales due to the extremely good sale prices. Although the prices are low, Kodo still plans to make a gross per unit profit of $50 for the Instamatic III and $100 for the Super XX. These are the goals Kodo has set, in order of their importance:

1.   Avoid underutilization of normal production capacity.

2.   Seek sales equal to or greater than the estimates. Kodo feels the sale of 35 mm cameras is twice as important as the sales of Instamatic III cameras because of the profit.

3.   Minimize the overtime operation of the factory as much as possible.

Formulate as an LGP problem.

3.12   The Tiny Toy Company makes three types of new toys: the tiny tank, the tiny truck, and the tiny turtle. Plastic used in one unit of each is 1.5, 2.0 and 1.0 pounds respectively. Rubber for one unit of each toy is 0.5, 0.5, and 1.0 pounds respectively. Also, each tank uses 0.3 pounds of metal and the truck uses 0.6 pounds of metal during production. The average weekly availability for plastic is 16,000 pounds, 9,000 pounds of metal, and 5,000 pounds of rubber. It takes two hours of labor to make one tank, two hours for one truck, and one hour for a turtle. The company allows no more than 40 hours a week for production. Finally, the cost of manufacturing one tank is $7, 1 truck is $5 and 1 turtle is $4; a target budget of $164,000 is initially used as a guideline for the company to follow.

1.   Minimize overutilization of the weekly available supply of materials used in making the toys, and place twice as much emphasis on the plastic.

2.   Minimize the under and overutilization of the budget. Maximize available labor hour usage.

Formulate as an LGP Model.

3.13   The Nocontrol Data Corporation is a manufacturing firm which produces two types of Rigid Magnetic Media for OEM customers. The first type is a 14″ disk called the "Superbyte," and the second type of media is a 7″ disk called the "Superbrat." The firm's production capacity is a total of 40 hours per week for both products. Both disk types also require three hours of production time. The expected sales for the next week are 150 Superbytes and 250 Superbrats. The profit on either type of disk is $30. The staff level production manager has detailed the following goals:

1.   Avoid underutilization of production time.

2.   Produce the expected disks if possible.

3.   If the workmanship error by production workers remain at the current level, the firm will have to work overtime to meet the expected sales. The staff level production manager would like to avoid operating the production lines on an overtime basis.

Formulate as an LGP model.

3.14   A club had to think of a project they could do that would maximize their profit. One of the most reasonable ideas they devised was to sell soda and ice cream bars at the local July 4th celebration. Each of the club members would be required to sell soda and ice cream at least two hours. Because they were trying to raise money for the club, no one was paid for the time they put in. The unit profit on each can of soda sold was 25¢, and 15¢ for each ice cream bar sold. The organization leader of the club set the following goals in order of importance for the project to be worth their time.

1.   Achieve a profit goal of $300 or more.

2.   Meet the sales goal of 650 ice cream bars. (It is more important to sell most of the ice cream bars because it would be harder to store whatever was left over.)

3.   Meet the sales goal of 750 cans of soda.

Formulate as an LGP model.

3.15   A farmer grows onions for commercial sales. He grows two qualities of onions. Anything over three inches in diameter is a top quality onion. Anything under three inches or with a double heart is a reject. The top quality onions are sold to the local grocery store for resale. The profit on a top quality 50-pound bag of onions is $1.90. The profit on a 50-pound bag of rejects is $.90. Normally, it takes one hour to fill a bag of top quality onions and four hours to fill a bag of rejects. The normal operation time for one day is eight hours.

Following is a list of goals in order of importance set by the onion farmer.

1.   Achieve the profit goal of $350 per day during harvest.

2.   Limit the overtime operation in the field to only two hours a day.

3.   Meet the sales goal of 145 top quality bags of onions. (The farmer feels it is more important to meet the sales goal of top quality onions than the goal for rejects.)

4.   Meet the sales goal of 75 reject bags of onions.

Formulate as an LGP model.

4

A Solution Procedure
For Linear Goal
Programming

■ 4.1 ■ Chapter Overview

This chapter presents a solution procedure designed to solve LGP problems. The step-by-step solution procedure is described and illustrated with sample problems. In addition, this chapter discusses several solution procedure complications and their resolution. Special topics such as an integer LGP solution procedure, a zero-one LGP solution procedure and sensitivity analysis are also presented.

■ 4.2 ■ An LGP Solution Procedure

To solve formulated LGP problems a new solution procedure developed by Schniederjans and Kwak[1] will be presented. This LGP procedure is based on the linear programming solution procedure presented in Chapter 2. The major feature of this modified simplex-based algorithm is that it does not require as many solution matrix (i.e., solution tableau) elements as earlier and more commonly used LGP solution procedures. The solution procedure is an iterative process involving the creation of a sequence of solution tableaus, similar to the solution procedure for linear programming. The reduction in computational elements in each tableau saves the

1. Schniederjans, Marc J., and Kwak, N.K., "An Alternative Solution Method for Goal Programming Problems: A Tutorial," *Journal of the Operational Research Society,* Vol. 33, No. 3 (March, 1982), pp. 247–251.

student computation time that the student can use in the interpretation stage of the solution process.

■ *Initial Tableau Formulation Procedure*

To begin, we must place the LGP problem formulation into a first tableau. A generalized initial tableau is presented below:

			$w_{kl} P_k$
			$x_j \quad d_i^-$
	Basis	Z	w_{kl}
$w_{kl} P_k$	d_i^+	$-b_i$	a_{ij}

where:

$w_{kl} P_k$ = an l row (or column) vector of differential weights attached to their respective k preemptive priorities

x_j = a row vector in ascending order of all decision variables

d_i^- = a row vector in ascending order of all negative deviational variables

Basis = a column heading that labels the basic variables in the solution

Z = a value that represents the total absolute deviation from all goals

w_{kl} = a row vector of differential weights

d_i^+ = a column vector in ascending order of all positive deviational variables. Similar to linear programming, variables in this column are called basic variables and all other variables are called zero variables or nonbasic variables.

$-b_i$ = a negatively signed column vector of all the right-hand-side values

a_{ij} = a matrix of all the technological coefficients in the appropriate row and under the appropriate variable

The following steps are suggested in setting up the initial tableau:

1. Draw necessary box configuration and label the solution basis column.

2. List the decision variable vector elements and negative deviational variable vector elements in ascending order, respectively.

3. List appropriate priorities and weights in their respective row vector. Variables not in the objective function are given a zero weight.

86

4. List positive deviational vector elements in the Basis column. Create necessary artificial deviational variables to permit initial problem setup.[2] In this format all the positive deviational variables are basic variables and all other variables are non-basic variables.

5. List the right-hand-side vector elements for each goal constraint. Place a negative sign in front of each element.[3]

6. List the appropriate preemptive priority and differential weight vector elements for each goal constraint in the solution basis. Create any additional priorities (i.e., $0P_0$) for the artificial deviational variables. Variables not in the objective function should be given a zero weight.

7. Solve for Z (total absolute deviation) in the initial problem formulation. This value is found by the following formula:

$$Z = \sum_{i=1}^{I} | w_{kl} \cdot -b_i | \qquad \textbf{(4.1)}$$

where:

I = number of goal constraints

w_{kl} = differential weight vector for each of d_i^+ priorities in the solution basis

$-b_i$ = right-hand-side vector elements

8. List the appropriate differential weighting under the x_j and d_i^- vector rows. Any variable not in the objective function should be given a zero weight.

9. List the appropriate technological coefficients in the appropriate row and under the appropriate variable column.

---

2. We have seen in Chapter 3 that some goal constraints do not require a positive deviational variable. When this occurs, we create an "artificial" positive deviational variable and place it in this column. The solution procedure requires each goal constraint to have a positive deviational variable. This artificial positive deviational variable must be removed from the solution basis during the iterative process. (If an artificial variable exists in the optimal solution basis, we have an "infeasible" LGP solution. An infeasible LGP solution will be discussed later in this chapter.) To accomplish this, we attach to each a differentially weighted priority (i.e., $0P_0$) that forces their removal. The zero weighting is always attached to these priorities to prevent the artificial variables from being included in the solution basis. The P_0 priority places the artificial variable at a higher priority than P_1. This approach is similar to the treatment of artificial variables in linear programming. If an LGP problem possesses any linear equality constraints, the same procedure as described above (i.e., add artificial d_i^+ at $0P_0$) is to be used in solving the problem.
3. If $x_j = 0$, and $x_j - d_i^+ = b_i$, then $d_i^+ = -b_i$.

Having utilized the nine steps above, the initial LGP tableau is complete.

Now let us interpret the result of the initial tableau. The solution basis can be read from the Basis and $-d_i^+$ column vectors. Initially, all $d_i^+ = -b_i$ and all x_j and $d_i^- = 0$. This solution is not optimal because the basic variables cannot be negative when the optimal solution is found. This would violate our non-negative requirement of $d_i^+ \geq 0$. Similar to the minimization solution procedure in linear programming, the existing solution can be improved upon as long as there are negative values in the $-b_i$ column vector. We must now proceed to revise and improve the solution.

■ Procedure for Revising the Tableau

To solve this problem from this point, a revision procedure for generating the next and all subsequent tableaus is required. This procedure is as follows:

1. *Determine which basic variable is to exit the solution basis.* This is accomplished by selecting the variable in the solution basis with the highest-ranked priority (i.e., $P_0 > P_1 >>> P_k$). Why? Because, by removing the variable from the solution basis, it becomes a non-basic variable equal to zero. The result is a reduction of deviation at the highest priority. If tied within a given priority level, the greatest differential weight determines the variable selection. When two or more variables have the same weighted priority level, selection is based on the variable that has the greatest negative right-hand-side value. If the priority, weight and right-hand-side values are tied, the selection may be arbitrary. This variable labels the pivot row.

2. *Determine which nonbasic variable is to enter the solution basis.* This is accomplished by selecting the column whose P_k is equal to or less than the P_k in the pivot row and that has the smallest resulting ratio when the positive technological coefficients in the pivot row are divided into their respective positive elements in the w_{kl} vector row. This variable labels the pivot column. Why do we select the column with the smallest resulting ratio? Because the column's ratio will contribute less weighted deviation to Z than any other. This is desirable, since we seek to minimize Z. In the case of a tie, select the variable with the highest priority. If tied within the same priority, selection should be based on the largest denominator value in the tied ratios (i.e., pivot row value). Beyond these measures, column selection is arbitrary. *Caution:* A condition called "continuous looping" can occur in any problem. This condition is caused by the repeated selection of the same pivot column in subsequent tableaus. That is, we continue to select the same pivot row and alter back-and-forth between the same pivot columns in all subsequent tableaus. This will not result in a solution to the LGP problem. To break out of the continuous

loop, select the next smallest ratio between the positive technological coefficient and the w_{kl} vector row elements.

3. *Set up a framework for the new tableau.* This is accomplished by drawing the necessary box configuration and exchanging the pivot row variables and pivot column variables. Also, the priority and differential weights attached to the variable brought into the solution basis should be placed in the appropriate position in the $w_{kl}P_k$ vectors of the new tableau. All other variables remain in their same places in the new tableau.

4. *Determine the new elements that correspond to the elements in the pivot row.* The element at the intersection of the pivot row and pivot column is called the *pivot element*. The new element that corresponds to the old pivot element is found by taking the reciprocal of the pivot element. All other elements in the row are found by dividing the pivot row elements by the pivot element and changing the resulting sign.

5. *Determine the new elements that correspond to the elements in the pivot column.* These elements are found by dividing the pivot column elements by the pivot element.

6. *Determining the other elements in the new tableau.* Except for the Z element representing total absolute deviation, all other elements are found by the following formula:

$$\text{new element} = \text{old element} - \left(\frac{\text{product of two corner elements}}{\text{pivot element}} \right) \quad \textbf{(4.2)}$$

The two corner elements are found by selecting respective elements out of the same pivot row and same pivot column as the *new element*. That is, the two corner elements are at the opposite corners of a square or rectangle formed by the corner elements of the *pivot element* and the *old element*.

7. *Determine the new total absolute deviation element.* This is accomplished by the following formula:

$$\text{New } Z = \sum_{i=1}^{I} | w_{kl} \cdot b_i^* | \quad \textbf{(4.3)}$$

where:

w_{kl} = the differential weight attached to only those deviational variables in the solution basis

b_i^* = the right-hand-side values in the solution basis during each iteration

8. *Determine if an optimal solution (i.e., best goal satisficing solution) has been reached.* The solution is optimal if the basic variables are all positive and one

or more of the w_{kl} row elements have a negative sign or the next variable to be brought into the solution basis is at a higher priority level. If we have negative basic variables, we do not have an optimal solution and we must repeat steps 1 through 8. If all the basic variables are positive but no values in objective function row are negative, the solution is not optimal and we must continue onto steps 9 and 10.

9. *Determine which variable is to exit the solution basis.* We accomplish this by selecting the variable at the highest priority level. The pivot element comes from this row. Use the differential weighting and largest positive right-hand-side value rules to break ties, if necessary.

10. *Determine which variable is to enter the solution basis.* This is accomplished by selecting the column that has the smallest resulting ratio when the negative coefficients in the pivot row are divided into their respective positive elements in the w_{kl} row, changing the resulting sign. This variable labels the pivot column. We can now repeat steps 3 through 8.

Once an optimal solution has been reached, the values for the x_j, d_i^-, d_i^+ and P_k can be read off the final tableau. The P_k values may require some additional minor computation if more than one deviation variable at the same priority level is in the solution basis.

■ 4.3 ■ Application of the LGP Solution Procedure

To illustrate the LGP solution procedure, we will now use it to solve two different problems. Students are encouraged to re-read the procedural steps as they are used to solve the applications in this section.

■ Application 1:

In Section 3.3, Problem 1, an LGP problem formulation for the Ollie Advertising Company was presented as follows:

$$\text{Minimize:} \quad Z = d_1^- + d_1^+ + d_2^+ + d_3^-$$

$$\begin{aligned}
\text{subject to:} \quad & x_1 + 3x_2 + d_1^- - d_1^+ = 300 \\
& x_1 \qquad\qquad - d_2^+ = 50 \\
& 2x_1 + 4x_2 + d_3^- \qquad = M
\end{aligned}$$

$$\text{and} \quad x_j, d_i^-, d_i^+ \geq 0$$

Using the initial tableau formulation procedure, this problem can be placed into the following initial tableau:

FIRST TABLEAU

		Basis	350	x_1	x_2	d_1^-	d_3^-
				0	0	$1P_1$	$1P_1$
				0	0	1	1
	$1P_1$	d_1^+	-300	1	3	1	0
	$1P_1$	d_2^+	-50	1	0	0	0
Pivot Row	$0P_0$	d_3^+	-400	2	(4)	0	1

(Pivot Column above x_2; $1P_1$ column header above right)

Several procedural observations should be made on this initial tableau formulation. First, since the third goal constraint did not have a positive deviational variable, an artificial variable, d_3^+, had to be created. Attached to that artificial variable is the zero weighted priority of $0P_0$. Second, the other deviational variables in this model were not prioritized or differentially weighted and as such were all equally desirable for inclusion in the solution basis. To express this situation in the tableau, we simply place all of these deviational variables at P_1 with an equal differential weight of one. Third, since the decision variables are not in the objective function, they receive a zero value in the w_{kl} row. Fourth, the value of M in the model is arbitrarily set at 400. This is a very large value that the sum of $2x_1 + 4x_2$ cannot exceed. Fifth, the right-hand-side elements in the tableau were given a negative sign and placed in the $-b_i$ vector column. Sixth, the Z value is calculated by using Equation 4.1 as follows:

$$Z = |1 \cdot -300| + |1 \cdot -50| + |0 \cdot -400| = 350$$

Finally, the remaining elements were simply taken from the goal constraints and placed in the appropriate row and column.

We can see in this first tableau that we do not have an optimal solution because of the negative right-hand-side values in the solution basis. So we must revise the tableau. To do this we will use the tableau revising procedure presented in Section 4.2. The resulting second tableau is as follows.

In the second tableau we have removed the artificial variable d_3^-. Once removed from the solution basis, it is never allowed to re-enter. Also, the value of Z was calculated by using Equation 4.3 as follows:

$$Z = |1 \cdot 0| + |1 \cdot -50| = 50$$

SECOND TABLEAU

			Pivot Column			
			0	$0P_0$	$1P_1$	$1P_1$
			x_1	d_3^+	d_1^-	d_3^-
	Basis	50	0	0	1	1
$1P_1$	d_1^+	0	$-\frac{1}{2}$	$\frac{3}{4}$	1	$-\frac{3}{4}$
Pivot Row $\qquad$ $1P_1$	d_2^+	-50	(1)	0	0	0
0	x_2	100	$-\frac{1}{2}$	$\frac{1}{4}$	0	$-\frac{1}{4}$

The negative d_2^+ value in the solution basis indicates that an optimal solution has not been reached. So we must continue repeating the tableau, revising steps to generate the third tableau, which is as follows:

THIRD TABLEAU

				Pivot Column		
			$1P_1$	$0P_0$	$1P_1$	$1P_1$
			d_2^+	d_3^+	d_1^-	d_3^-
	Basis	25	0	0	1	1
Pivot Row $\qquad$ $1P_1$	d_1^+	-25	$-\frac{1}{2}$	$\frac{3}{4}$	(1)	$-\frac{3}{4}$
0	x_1	50	1	0	0	0
0	x_2	75	$-\frac{1}{2}$	$\frac{1}{4}$	0	$-\frac{1}{4}$

Again, we do not have an optimal solution, so we repeat the tableau revising steps to generate the following fourth tableau:

FOURTH TABLEAU

			$1P_1$	$0P_0$	$1P_1$	$1P_1$
			d_2^+	d_3^+	d_1^+	d_3^-
	Basis	25	$\frac{1}{2}$	$-\frac{3}{4}$	1	$\frac{1}{4}$
$1P_1$	d_1^-	25	$\frac{1}{2}$	$\frac{3}{4}$	1	$\frac{3}{4}$
0	x_1	50	1	0	0	0
0	x_2	75	$-\frac{1}{2}$	$\frac{1}{4}$	0	$-\frac{1}{4}$

In this fourth tableau we have arrived at an optimal solution. This is so because the right-hand-side values are all positive and there is a negative value in the w_{kl} row vector. The optimal solution is where $x_1 = 50$ (i.e., radio commercials to place) and $x_2 = 75$ (i.e., television commercials to place). We can also see that we have achieved two of the three goals of the model. The $d_1^- = 25$ must be multiplied by 1000 since we earlier divided this goal constraint by 1000. The $d_1^- = 25$ indicates that only $275,000 (i.e., $300 - 25 = 275$ times 1000) of the $300,000 budget will be necessary. So we underutilize the budgetary goal of $300,000. The goal of placing 50 radio spots at minimum was achieved, and the goal of obtaining 400 additional sales as a result of the new product promotion was also achieved. (Had we selected a value for M smaller than 400, we would have had to change the third goal constraint to include a d_3^+ variable. Students are encouraged to change M and resolve the problem to determine the effect it will have on the solution.)

■ Application 2:

In Section 3.3, Problem 2, an LGP problem formulation for the Florance Manufacturing Company was presented as follows:

$$\text{Minimize:} \quad Z = P_1 d_1^+ + P_2 d_2^- + P_2 d_3^- + P_3 d_2^+ + P_3 d_3^+ + P_4 d_4^+$$

$$\text{subject to:} \quad 3x_1 + 3x_2 + d_1^- - d_1^+ = 120$$
$$x_1 \qquad\qquad + d_2^- - d_2^+ = 10$$
$$x_2 + d_3^- - d_3^+ = 15$$
$$x_1 \qquad\qquad - d_4^+ = 5$$

$$\text{and} \qquad x_j, d_i^-, d_i^+ \geq 0$$

To solve this LGP problem, we must put the model into its initial tableau as follows:

FIRST TABLEAU
Pivot Column

				0	0	0	$1P_2$	$1P_2$
				x_1	x_2	d_1^-	d_2^-	d_3^-
		Basis	150	0	0	0	1	1
Pivot Row	$1P_1$	d_1^+	-120	③	3	1	0	0
	$1P_3$	d_2^+	-10	1	0	0	1	0
	$1P_3$	d_3^+	-15	0	1	0	0	1
	$1P_4$	d_4^+	-5	1	0	0	0	0

Several procedural observations should be made on this initial tableau. First, the problem has multiple priority levels but no differential weighting. So, we will place a weight of one in front of non-weighted priorities. Second, the d_1^- variable is not in the objective function, and like the decision variables will be given a zero value in the $w_{kl}P_k$ and w_{kl} row vectors. Third, Z was calculated using Equation 4.1 as follows:

$$Z = |1 \cdot -120| + |1 \cdot -10| + |1 \cdot -15| + |1 \cdot -5| = 150$$

Finally, the other remaining elements were placed in the tableau in the appropriate rows and columns.

Since the negative right-hand-side values indicate we do not have an optimal solution, we must continue on to the next tableau. Utilizing the tableau revision procedure, the resulting second tableau is as follows:

SECOND TABLEAU

					Pivot Column			
				$1P_1$	0	0	$1P_2$	$1P_2$
				d_1^+	x_2	d_1^-	d_2^-	d_3^-
		Basis	80	0	0	0	1	1
	0	x_1	40	⅓	−1	−⅓	0	0
	$1P_3$	d_2^+	30	⅓	−1	−⅓	1	0
Pivot Row	$1P_3$	d_3^+	−15	0	(1)	0	0	1
	$1P_4$	d_4^+	35	⅓	−1	−⅓	0	0

Again we do not have an optimal tableau and must compute the following third and fourth tableaus:

THIRD TABLEAU

					Pivot Column			
				$1P_1$	$1P_3$	0	$1P_2$	$1P_2$
				d_1^+	d_3^+	d_1^-	d_2^-	d_3^-
		Basis	35	0	0	0	1	1
	0	x_1	25	⅓	−1	−⅓	0	1
Pivot Row	$1P_3$	d_2^+	15	⅓	(−1)	−⅓	1	1
	0	x_2	15	0	1	0	0	−1
	$1P_4$	d_4^+	20	⅓	−1	−⅓	0	1

FOURTH TABLEAU

			Pivot Column			
			$1P_1$	$1P_3$	0	$1P_2$	$1P_2$
			d_1^+	d_2^+	d_1^-	d_2^-	d_3^-
	Basis	20	0	0	0	1	1
0	x_1	10	0	1	0	-1	0
Pivot Row — $1P_3$	d_3^+	15	$\frac{1}{3}$	-1	$\left(-\frac{1}{3}\right)$	1	0
0	x_2	30	$\frac{1}{3}$	-1	$-\frac{1}{3}$	1	0
$1P_4$	d_4^+	5	0	1	0	-1	0

In the third tableau we bring d_3^+ into the solution basis and take d_2^+ out. In the fourth tableau we can see that if we follow the solution procedure we would bring d_2^+ back into the solution basis and take d_3^+ out. This problem complication we referred to in Section 4.2 as a "continuous loop." As suggested, we can break the loop by selecting the next most likely candidate for a pivot column, d_1^-. Pivoting off this column allows us to generate the fifth tableau as follows:

FIFTH TABLEAU

			$1P_1$	$1P_3$	$1P_3$	$1P_2$	$1P_2$
			d_1^+	d_2^+	d_3^+	d_2^-	d_3^-
	Basis	5	0	0	0	1	1
0	x_1	10	0	1	0	-1	0
0	d_1^-	45	1	-3	-3	3	3
0	x_2	15	0	0	-1	0	-1
$1P_4$	d_4^+	5	0	1	0	-1	0

Since this fifth tableau has no negative w_{kl} row values, it appears to be optimal. But in accordance with the tableau revision procedure presented in Section 4.2 we can see that it is optimal. Given the next pivot row of d_4^+, we must select a pivot column. The only candidate is d_2^-, but this column variable is at a higher priority (i.e., $P_2 > P_4$) than any other variable in the solution basis. Therefore, we cannot pivot off this column, and we have achieved an optimal solution.

The solution for this manufacturing company problem is as follows: $x_1 = 10$ (i.e., production in units of Product A) and $x_2 = 15$ (i.e., production in units of Product B). The top three goals (i.e., P_1 = Profit target, P_2 = Product A production

95

and P_3 = Product B production) were fully satisfied. The fourth goal (i.e., P_4 = Minimizing over production of Product A from a minimum production level) was not fully satisfied. The value of P_4 is 5, which can be read off the solution basis since $d_4^+ = 5$ and d_4^+ is attached to P_4.

The two problems solved in this section were used to illustrate the LGP solution procedure. These problems also illustrated several solution procedure complications: a tie in the variables to exit the solution basis, a tie in the variables to enter the solution basis, artificial variables and priorities, and "continuous looping." As we will see in Section 4.4, there are other solution procedure complications.

■ 4.4 ■ Solution Procedure Complications

In addition to the procedural complications previously illustrated, we can experience other solution procedure complications, which include alternative optimal solutions, unbounded solutions, infeasible solutions and negative right-hand-side values.

■ Alternative Optimal Solutions

It is possible to have an alternative optimal solution, that is, an alternative set of decision variables or deviational variables that result in the same goal achievement satisficing solution. An alternative optimal solution is present in an LGP problem if, in the optimal solution basis, we can exchange variables without altering goal achievement at any priority level.

To determine if an LGP problem has an alternative solution involves the following steps:

1. Select all pivot columns from the optimal solution basis whose w_{kl} row elements (i.e., elements below column variables) are zero. If none of the w_{kl} row elements have a zero value, no alternative optimal solution exists. If one or more of the columns have zero values, they represent possible candidates as pivot columns for an additional iteration that will derive an alternative solution. If one or more zeros occur, continue on to step 2.

2. Eliminate some or all of the column candidates found in step 1 by dropping columns that do not have any eligible pivot elements (i.e., matching $-b_i$ and a_{ij} or b_i and $-a_{ij}$, which is necessary to determine a pivot column). If all of the column candidates are eliminated, no alternative solution exists. If one or more candidates still exist, continue to step 3.

3. Determine the pivot row, if one exists, by the same procedure described in Section 4.2. We would exclude from consideration all pivot rows whose existing

variable has a priority that would violate the existing solution's given levels of goal achievement. If all of the eligible row variables cannot be exchanged without altering the levels of goal achievement, we do not have an alternative solution. If a row's variable can be exchanged, we have determined the pivot row and the subsequent pivot column for the next iteration. We then would continue to step 4.

4. Having determined the pivot column and pivot row, use the LGP solution procedure presented in Section 4.2 to determine the next tableau. The solution generated in the next tableau will be an alternative optimal solution. If multiple optimal solutions exist, they can be found by repeating steps 1 through 4 for each subsequent tableau that generates a differing solution.

In practice, an alternative solution is a desirable problem complication. The additional tableau is informationally valuable to any decision maker. The extra effort to compute an alternative solution is often more than paid back by the increased discretion in solution choice. Indeed, for problems where multiple solutions exist, decision makers are afforded the opportunity to bring into the decision process other relevant non-quantifiable criteria to make a final choice among the alternative solutions.

■ Unbounded Solutions

An unbounded solution occurs in linear programming because of the inflexibility of right-hand-side values to define a feasible solution zone consistent with a single objective solution criteria. In LGP, we seek a satisficing solution that allows for some flexibility in right-hand-side values. So, LGP problems will not generate unbounded solutions.

■ Infeasible Solutions

An infeasible solution occurs in linear programming and LGP when a constraint is violated. We can observe this in an LGP solution where an artificial variable is left in an optimal solution basis. Since an artificial variable in an optimal solution represents impossible or infeasible deviation, the solution is infeasible. When an infeasible solution occurs, it is usually related to inaccurate model formulation. Students should closely examine all goal constraints to determine if they should be adjusted, dropped or new ones added.

■ Negative Right-Hand-Side Values

LGP solution procedures and most linear programming computer programs cannot solve problems that have negative right-hand-side values. The reason is because the negative right-hand-side value prohibits pivot row selection and generally disrupts pivoting logic. The simple solution to this problem is to multiply the entire goal constraint by a -1. This adjustment does not change the resulting solution but does permit the goal constraint to be included in the solution process.

The solution complication procedures presented in this section help us solve LGP problems for any d_i^- and d_i^+ values greater than or equal to zero. In the two problems presented in Section 4.3, integer variable values resulted but were not guaranteed by the solution procedure presented. If a non-integer solution had resulted, and an integer solution was desirable, a solution revising procedure to derive an integer solution would be necessary. In Section 4.5, a procedure to derive integer solutions is presented.

■ 4.5 ■ An Integer LGP
Solution Procedure

There are several integer LGP solution procedures. Students are encouraged to reference Section 1.3 ("Miscellaneous References") to review prior research describing these various methods. Some of these methods, such as the cutting-plane method, implicit enumeration and the branch-and-bound method are modified versions of integer linear prgramming solution procedures. Of these methods, we will use a branch-and-bound type LGP solution procedure.

■ *Solution Procedure*

The branch-and-bound method to be presented for solving integer LGP problems can be used where the decision variable values are required to be all integer or where only select variables are required to be integer. The procedure involves the reformulation of LGP problems and the repeated use of the LGP solution procedure presented in Section 4.2. An integer solution is eventually forced to occur due to the reformulation of the problem, not because of the solution procedure. So, what is important in solving for an integer LGP solution is to know how to adjust the formulation of the problem, and to know when an optimal solution has been achieved. To aid in solving integer LGP problems, the following branch-and-bound solution procedural steps are presented:

1. Solve the original LGP problem using the solution procedure presented in Section 4.2. If the resulting solution satisfies the integer problem requirement, stop. If the solution does not satisfy the integer problem requirements, continue to the next step.

2. Select the non-integer decision variable with the largest fraction and develop

two goal constraints to bind the decision variable. These constraints can be formulated as follows:

$$x_j + d_i^- = \text{decision variable value rounded down to} \quad \textbf{(4.4)}$$
$$\text{the next integer value}$$
$$x_j - d_i^+ = \text{decision variable value rounded up to} \quad \textbf{(4.5)}$$
$$\text{the next integer value.}$$

3. Add the new goal constraint from Equation 4.4 to the original LGP problem. Place the d_i^- variable at P_0 in the objective function and solve this new problem. This new problem is called a *branch problem* because it branches off the original problem.

4. Add the new goal constraint from Equation 4.5 to the original LGP problem. Place the d_i^+ at P_0 in the objective function and solve this second new problem.

5. The solutions to either of the branch problems generated in steps 3 and 4 must be interpreted.

    a. If both result in integer solutions, select the one that provides the greatest goal accomplishment. The optimal integer solution to the original problem has been achieved and no further steps are necessary.

    b. If one branch solution is integer and the other branch solution is a non-integer solution that is less satisficing then the integer solution, the optimal integer solution has been achieved and no further steps are necessary.[4]

    c. If one branch solution is integer and the other branch solution is a non-integer solution that is more satisficing than the integer solution, continue to step 6. The integer solution is an acceptable candidate for an optimal solution.

    d. If both branch solutions are non-integer, continue to step 6.

    e. If any branch problem generates an infeasible solution, that branch is at an end and no subsequent problems can be formulated from it.

6. For each branch solution that is non-integer, repeat steps 2, 3, 4, and 5 using another non-integer decision variable.

7. Continue to repeat step 6 until the necessary integer values for the decision variables are obtained. If multiple integer solutions exist, the overall optimal solution can then be selected from all of the acceptable integer solutions on the basis of goal accomplishment. That is, the solution that is integer and provides the greatest goal accomplishment is the optimal solution.

---

4. Similar to the branch-and bound technique for linear programming problems, the addition of constraints to an LGP problem can only result in equal-to or less satisficing solutions in subsequent branching problems. So continued branching is needless.

To illustrate the use of this solution procedure, the next section presents its application in resolving an integer LGP problem.

■ Application

Suppose we have the following integer LGP problem:

$$\text{Minimize:} \quad Z = P_1(d_2^- + d_2^+ + d_3^- + d_3^+) + P_2(d_1^-)$$
$$\text{subject to:} \quad 300x_1 + 200x_2 + d_1^- = 13000$$
$$5x_1 + 2x_2 + d_2^- - d_2^+ = 180$$
$$3x_1 + 3x_2 + d_3^- - d_3^+ = 141$$
$$\text{and} \quad x_j \geq 0 \text{ and all integer}$$
$$d_i^-, d_i^+ \geq 0$$

We can see in the formulation that all x_j decision variables must be integer. To begin the integer LGP solution procedure we solve the original problem using the usual LGP solution procedure (i.e., step 1). In Figure 4.1, the original problem's solution (labeled Problem 1) is presented. Neither of the decision variables are integer. So we must create two new goal constraints (step 2) by branching off of x_1. In the Problem 2 formulation below, we can see the new goal constraint is added (step 3):

$$\text{Minimize:} \quad Z = 0P_0\, d_4^- + P_1\, (d_2^- + d_2^+ + d_3^- + d_3^+)\, P_2(d_1^-)$$
$$\text{subject to:} \quad 300x_1 + 200x_2 + d_1^- = 13000$$
$$5x_1 + 2x_2 + d_2^- - d_2^+ = 180$$
$$3x_1 + 3x_2 + d_3^- - d_3^+ = 141$$
$$x_1 + d_4^- = 28$$
$$\text{and} \quad x_j, d_i^-, d_i^+ \geq 0$$

This problem's solution is also presented in Figure 4.1. Similarly, we formulate Problem 3 as stated below (step 4):

$$\text{Minimize:} \quad Z = 0P_0 d_4^+ + P_1(d_2^+ + d_3^- + d_3^+) + P_2(d_1^-)$$
$$\text{subject to:} \quad 300x_1 + 200x_2 + d_1^- = 13000$$
$$5x_1 + 2x_2 + d_2^- - d_2^+ = 180$$
$$3x_1 + 3x_2 + d_3^- - d_3^+ = 141$$
$$x_1 - d_4^+ = 29$$
$$\text{and} \quad x_i, d_i^-, d_i^+ \geq 0$$

The solution to Problem 3 is also presented in Figure 4.1

Problem 2 resulted in an all integer solution with a P_1 of 2. Problem 3 resulted in only a partial integer solution but with a P_1 of 1.5. If Problem 2's P_1 was less

Figure 4.1 Optimal Branching Solutions

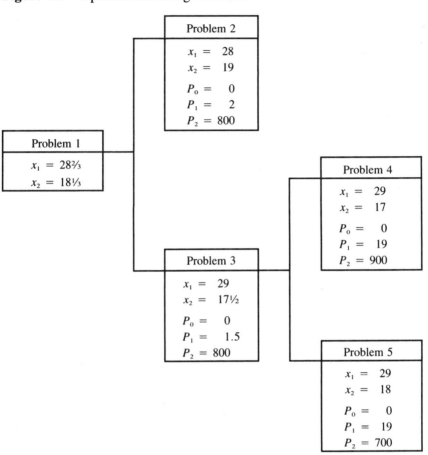

than Problem 3's P_1, then we could accept the solution to Problem 2 as optimal (step 5). Since Problem 2's P_1 is greater than Problem 3's P_1, we must continue to branch off the non-integer solution to determine if an integer solution superior to Problem 2 exists (step 6). The formulation for Problem 4 is as follows:

Minimize: $Z = 0P_0 (d_4^+ + d_5^-) + P_1 (d_2^- + d_2^+ + d_3^- + d_3^+) + P_2(d_1^-)$

subject to:
$$300x_1 + 200x_2 + d_1^- = 13000$$
$$5x_1 + 3x_2 + d_2^- - d_2^+ = 180$$
$$3x_1 + 3x_2 + d_3^- - d_3^+ = 141$$
$$x_1 - d_4^+ = 29$$
$$x_2 + d_5^- = 17$$

and $x_j, d_i^-, d_i^+ \geq 0$

The formulation for Problem 5 is as follows:

Minimize: $Z = 0P_0 (d_4^+ + d_5^+) + P_1(d_2^- + d_2^+ + d_3^- + d_3^+) + P_2(d_1^-)$

subject to:
$$300x_1 + 200x_2 + d_1^- = 13000$$
$$5x_1 + 3x_2 + d_2^- - d_2^+ = 180$$
$$3x_1 + 3x_2 + d_3^- - d_3^+ = 141$$
$$x_1 - d_4^+ = 29$$
$$x_2 - d_5^+ = 18$$

and $x_j, d_i^-, d_i^+ \geq 0$

The solutions to these two new branches are also presented in Figure 4.1. We can see that the solution for Problem 4 is integer but the P_1 is greater than P_1 in Problem 2. So, this branch is at an end because further branching will not decrease the value of P_1. Also, the branch in Problem 5 is similarly at an end. The optimal solution in this problem is then given to us by the solution for Problem 2. This solution is the best all-integer solution (step 7).

In this section, we have seen how to generate integer solutions for LGP problems. Some integer problems require their decision variables to be either zero or one in the optimal solution basis. These types of integer LGP problems require a more specialized solution procedure. This specialized solution method is called a zero-one LGP solution procedure.

■ 4.6 ■ A Zero-One LGP Solution Procedure

When an LGP model requires some or all of its decision variables in its optimal solution basis to be either zero or one, we need to use a zero-one LGP solution approach. There are several zero-one LGP solution procedures, all of which are based on zero-one linear programming procedures. These zero-one LGP solution procedures include implicit enumeration and branch-and-bound methods. Students are encouraged to review the related research listed in Section 1.3. The Garrod and Moores (1978) study listed in Section 1.3, "Miscellaneous References," is illustrative of the implicit enumeration zero-one LGP solution procedure. Two other interesting applications of zero-one LGP are the Keown and Martin (1978) study and the Keown, Taylor and Duncan (1978) study, both listed in "Finance Related References."

One of the most common solution approaches for zero-one LGP problems is the branch-and-bound method. Unfortunately, zero-one LGP problem solutions require a significant amount of computational effort. Even small integer LGP problems are very computationally time-consuming when the branch-and-bound solution procedure is used. To reduce the computational requirements in *solving* a zero-one problem, greater care in *formulating* the problem to satisfy the zero-one solution requirements must be given. This may, in some zero-one problems, require the addition of goal constraints to the original zero-one LGP problem prior to initiating a branch-and-bound solution procedure. The formulation of these additional goal constraints depends on our understanding of the problem. That is, we must thoroughly understand the zero-one solution requirements of the problem and use this understanding to generate additional goal constraints that will force the zero-one solution we desire.

■ *Solution Procedure*

Zero-one LGP problem situations can differ significantly in complexity and require differing amounts of computational effort for a branch-and-bound solution procedure. Each problem situation will provide opportunities for insightful modelers to minimize their computational effort by creating additional goal constraints to force a desired zero-one solution with the least number of branching problems. The procedure for solving a zero-one LGP problem is as follows:

1. Formulate the basic zero-one LGP problem.

2. Develop any additional goal constraints that may further bind the decision variables to a value of zero or one.

3. Solve the basic problem in step 1 including the addition of goal constraints from step 2. If the resulting solution satisfies the zero-one LGP solution requirements, the optimal solution has been achieved and no further steps are necessary. If the resulting solution does not satisfy the zero-one LGP solution requirements, continue to step 4.

4. Use the branch-and-bound procedure presented in Section 4.5 to solve for an optimal zero-one solution, specifically, using the branching problems to force the decision variables to zero or one.

To illustrate this multi-step zero-one LGP solution procedure, let's use it to solve a salesperson routing problem.

■ *Application*

Problem situation: A salesperson must visit each of four cities. This salesperson is currently in one of the cities. The distances between each city are presented in Table 4.1. The salesperson has the following goals:

1. Visit each of the four cities.

2. Minimize traveling distance in miles.

Problem Formulation and Solution: The formulation of this routing problem can be expressed as a zero-one LGP problem as follows (step 1):

Minimize: $Z = P_1(d_1^- + \cdots + d_8^- + d_1^+ + \cdots + d_8^+) + P_2(d_9^+)$

Subject to:
$$x_{12} + x_{13} + x_{14} + d_1^- - d_1^+ = 1$$
$$x_{21} + x_{23} + x_{24} + d_2^- - d_2^+ = 1$$
$$x_{31} + x_{32} + x_{34} + d_3^- - d_3^+ = 1$$
$$x_{41} + x_{43} + x_{43} + d_4^- - d_4^+ = 1$$
$$x_{21} + x_{31} + x_{41} + d_5^- - d_5^+ = 1$$
$$x_{12} + x_{32} + x_{42} + d_6^- - d_6^+ = 1$$
$$x_{13} + x_{23} + x_{43} + d_7^- - d_7^+ = 1$$
$$x_{14} + x_{24} + x_{34} + d_8^- - d_8^+ = 1$$
$$10x_{12} + \cdots + x_{43} \qquad - d_9^+ = 0$$

and $\qquad x_{ij} = 0$ or 1

In this model, x_{ij} represents the salesperson's routing assignment between the *i*th city and the *j*th city. If $x_{ij} = 1$ then the salesperson should travel between the particular cities *i* and *j*. If $x_{ij} = 0$, then the salesperson should not be assigned to travel between the particular cities *i* and *j*.

Table 4.1
Traveling Distance in Hundreds of Miles
Between Each of the Four Cities

	City			
City	1	2	3	4
1	–	10	5	3
2	10	–	7	2
3	5	7	–	1
4	3	2	1	–

As formulated, this problem does not insure a zero-one solution if solved using the LGP solution procedure presented in Section 4.2. To improve its chances of obtaining a zero-one solution some additional goal constraints can be added (step 2). We can see in Table 4.1 that a routing assignment from City 2 to City 1 and from City 1 to City 2 are the same basic trip. Logically then, an assignment between Cities 1 and 2 should only be made once or not at all. Otherwise, the salesperson would not visit all four cities. We can express a goal constraint to prohibit the double assignment between Cities 1 and 2 as follows:

$$x_{12} + x_{21} + d_{10}^- = 1$$

The other similar city trip combinations can be formulated as follows:

$$x_{13} + x_{31} + d_{11}^- = 1$$
$$x_{14} + x_{41} + d_{12}^- = 1$$
$$x_{23} + x_{32} + d_{13}^- = 1$$
$$x_{24} + x_{42} + d_{14}^- = 1$$
$$x_{34} + x_{43} + d_{15}^- = 1$$

Since these additional goal constraints are related to the P_1 goal, they should be placed in that priority level. The effect of these additional constraints is not only to reflect the realities of the problem situation, but also to place greater pressure on the problem to generate a zero-one solution. The goal constraints 10 through 15 do not generate a zero-one solution, but may force the decision variable values closer to zero or one because they eliminate many alternative solution combinations for the x_{ij} variables.

Consistent with our zero-one LGP solution procedure, we now solve the 15 goal constraint LGP problem (step 3). The resulting solution turns out to be zero-one (i.e., $x_{12} = 1$, $x_{24} = 1$, $x_{31} = 1$, $x_{43} = 1$ and all other $x_{ij} = 0$). Since no branch-and-bound goal constraints were required (step 4), the zero-one solution can be accepted as an optimal solution. If one or more of the decision variables were not zero or one, the first zero-one solution would not have been the optimal one. We then would have used the branch-and-bound solution procedure to determine the optimality of any zero-one LGP solution. The branching constraints for the zero-one problem are:

$$x_j + d_i^- = 0 \tag{4.6}$$
$$x_j - d_i^+ = 1 \tag{4.7}$$

Substituting Equations 4.6 and 4.7 for Equations 4.4 and 4.5 are adjustments necessary to solve a zero-one problem using the branch-and-bound solution procedure presented in Section 4.5.

In this section, we have seen how to force a zero-one solution by making changes (i.e., adding goal constraints) to the original problem formulation. In effect, we made changes in a model to cause an acceptable solution. In the next section we again make changes in a model to result in a possibly "more" acceptable solution. This post-solution changing process is called *sensitivity analysis*.

■ 4.7 ■ LGP Sensitivity Analysis

One of the most common post-solution analysis techniques is sensitivity analysis. Many types of LGP sensitivity analyses exist and students are encouraged to review the literature on the subject. (The Rifai (1980) and Steuer (1979) studies are very illustrative.) We will examine sensitivity analysis of the P_k values. Sensitivity of

P_k seeks to explain what the effect of changing the order of the preemptive priorities will have on an existing optimal solution.

To conduct this sensitivity analysis we must first determine how many different ordering combinations exist for some K number of preemptive priority levels. Since we are taking K levels, K at a time, the formula to determine the number of possible priority orderings is $K!$ (i.e., K factorial). For example, if we had a three priority level LGP model, we can have as many as six orderings (i.e., $3! = 3 \cdot 2 \cdot 1$) of the preemptive priorities. These six can be enumerated as follows:

Position in the Objective Function	Orderings					
	1	2	3	4	5	6
1	P_1	P_1	P_2	P_2	P_3	P_3
2	P_2	P_3	P_1	P_3	P_1	P_2
3	P_3	P_2	P_3	P_1	P_2	P_1

Once the priorities have been enumerated it is necessary to reorder the priorities in the model. This involves shifting the deviational variables in the objective function around for each reordering of the priorities, creating as many different versions of the LGP model as there are reorderings.

We then solve each of these different models to determine the effect on the existing optimal solution variables and goal achievement. This brings us to why we go through all of this post-solution analysis. One or more of the revised solution models may, in fact, provide a more satisficing solution than the original LGP solution. Since the ordering of the priority levels is usually subjectively or intuitively derived, changes in the P_k are usually at the decision-maker's discretion anyway. Making changes in the P_k that generate a solution that better satisfies the problem (i.e., the decision maker) may very well be worth the extra analysis. Sometimes, though, the changing of P_k may not change the existing solution at all.

To illustrate the P_k sensitivity analysis procedure, let's examine the Swifter Trucking Company problem presented in Section 3.3, Problem 3. This problem has four priority levels, which means we can rearrange those four P_k levels 24 (i.e., $4! = 4 \cdot 3 \cdot 2 \cdot 1$) different ways. In Table 4.2, all 24 combinations of reordered priorities and their resulting solutions are presented.

We can see that even though 24 different LGP problems were solved, only three different sets of variable values resulted. The other 21 solutions are simply duplicate values. The reordering of P_k only resulted in shifting the minimized deviation for the three different solutions around to different goal levels.

These revised model solutions provide useful decision-making information. To illustrate, let's look at the Swifter Truck Company solutions for Model 1 and Model 2 in Table 4.2. In the solution for Model 1, we have fully satisfied the first three goals (i.e., Truck Demand, Legal Problems, and Union Problems) but to do this

Table 4.2
Sensitivity Analysis on All Combinations of P_k for the Swifters Trucking Problem*

	Goal	Revised Model Combinations											
		1	2	3	4	5	6	7	8	9	10	11	12
Priority Order and Resulting Goal Achievement	1	$P_1 = 0$	$P_1 = 0$	$P_1 = 0$	$P_1 = 0$	$P_1 = 0$	$P_1 = 0$	$P_2 = 0$	$P_2 = 0$	$P_2 = 0$	$P_2 = 0$	$P_2 = 0$	$P_2 = 0$
	2	$P_2 = 0$	$P_2 = 0$	$P_3 = 0$	$P_3 = 0$	$P_4 = 7150$	$P_4 = 7150$	$P_1 = 0$	$P_1 = 0$	$P_3 = 0$	$P_3 = 0$	$P_4 = 0$	$P_4 = 0$
	3	$P_3 = 0$	$P_4 = 7150$	$P_2 = 0$	$P_4 = 8725$	$P_2 = 0$	$P_3 = 6$	$P_3 = 0$	$P_4 = 7150$	$P_1 = 0$	$P_4 = 0$	$P_1 = 60.4$	$P_3 = 0$
	4	$P_4 = 8725$	$P_3 = 6$	$P_4 = 8725$	$P_2 = 0$	$P_3 = 6$	$P_2 = 0$	$P_4 = 8725$	$P_3 = 0$	$P_4 = 8725$	$P_1 = 60.4$	$P_3 = 0$	$P_1 = 60.4$
				Same as Model 1	Same as Model 1	Same as Model 2	Same as Model 2	Same as Model 1	Same as Model 2	Same as Model 1		Same as Model 10	Same as Model 10

Decision Variable Values

Model 1:
$x_1 = 6$, $x_6 = 3$, $x_7 = 6$, $x_8 = 3$, $x_{11} = 3$, $x_{13} = 1$, $x_{14} = 2$, $x_{15} = 6$

Model 2:
$x_1 = 6$, $x_6 = 6$, $x_7 = 6$, $x_{13} = 4$, $x_{14} = 2$, $x_{15} = 6$

Deviational Variable Values

Model 1:
$d_{11}^+ = 8725$, $d_{10}^+ = 6$

Model 2:
$d_{11}^+ = 7150$

Model 10:
$d_1^- = 6$, $d_2^- = 12$, $d_3^- = 12$, $d_3^+ = 12$, $d_5^+ = 6$, $d_6^+ = 4$, $d_7^+ = 2$, $d_8^+ = 6$

*All variables not listed are equal to zero

Table 4.2 (continued)

Revised Model Combinations

	Goal	13	14	15	16	17	18	19	20	21	22	23	24
Priority Order and Resulting Goal Achievement	1	$P_3 = 3$	$P_3 = 0$	$P_3 = 0$	$P_3 = 0$	$P_3 = 0$	$P_3 = 0$	$P_4 = 0$	$P_4 = 0$	$P_4 = 0$	$P_4 = 0$	$P_4 = 0$	$P_4 = 0$
	2	$P_1 = 0$	$P_1 = 0$	$P_2 = 0$	$P_2 = 0$	$P_4 = 0$	$P_4 = 0$	$P_1 = 60.4$	$P_1 = 60.4$	$P_2 = 0$	$P_2 = 0$	$P_3 = 0$	$P_3 = 0$
	3	$P_2 = 0$	$P_2 = 7150$	$P_1 = 0$	$P_4 = 0$	$P_1 = 60.4$	$P_2 = 0$	$P_2 = 0$	$P_3 = 0$	$P_1 = 60.4$	$P_3 = 0$	$P_1 = 60.4$	$P_1 = 60.4$
	4	$P_4 = 8725$	$P_4 = 0$	$P_4 = 8725$	$P_1 = 60.4$	$P_2 = 0$	$P_1 = 60.4$	$P_3 = 0$	$P_2 = 0$	$P_3 = 0$	$P_1 = 60.4$	$P_2 = 0$	$P_2 = 0$
Goal Achievement		Same as Model 1	Same as Model 2	Same as Model 1	Same as Model 10	Same as Model 10	Same as Model 10	Same as Model 10	Same as Model 10	Same as Model 10	Same as Model 10	Same as Model 10	Same as Model 10
Decision Variable Values													
Deviational Variable Values													

we have had to spend $8725 above our goal of $0. In Model 2, we have fully satisfied the first two goals (i.e., Truck Demand and Legal Problems) but we had to spend $7150 above our third goal value of $0 and violate our union contract by letting Distribution Center I receive 6 more trucks than Distribution Center III. The Model 1 solution fully satisfied three goals and the Model 2 solution only fully satisfied two goals. On the other hand, if $1575 ($8725 − $7150) is worth the trouble of violating the union contract, then Model 2 is a superior solution. In either case, decision makers are provided with additional information on solution alternatives and the costs of those alternatives.

As we have seen, post-solution analysis is time-consuming. But the informational value of the time invested usually pays for itself by providing new alternative solutions that better satisfy the problem situation. In actual practice, few researchers completely solve all enumerated problems. Why? Because most of the real-world problem situations do not permit all enumerated problems to realistically apply. So the researcher can simply eliminate any combination that is not permissible, saving considerable analysis.

Students are encouraged to review the prior research on this use of P_k sensitivity analysis listed in Section 1.3. Of particular illustrative value are the Lee, Green and Kim (1981) and Neely, Sellers and North (1980) studies listed in Section 1.3, "Management Related References." Both discuss and utilize P_k sensitivity analysis.

■ 4.8 ■ Summary

Presented in this chapter is a solution procedure for solving LGP problems. Also discussed was the use of the LGP solution procedure for integer LGP problems, a solution procedure for zero-one LGP problems and a procedure for sensitivity analysis.

The reduced element solution procedure presented in this chapter is particularly easy to use when solving small LGP problems by hand. Unfortunately, real-world problems can rarely be modeled in small-size problems. Students are encouraged to review the applications referenced in the bibliography in Section 1.3 to better understand the size of real-world problems. To solve larger LGP problems, computers are used. In the next chapter, two computer programs (i.e., for macro and micro computer systems) and their coding information are presented to handle various sized problems.

KEY VOCABULARY

Alternative solution	Continuous looping
Artificial variables	Infeasible solution
Basic variables	Integer solution
Branch-and-bound technique	Non-basic variables

109

Pivot column Tableau

Pivot row Unbounded solution

Sensitivity analysis Zero-one solution

Solution basis

CHAPTER QUESTIONS

4.1 If an LGP problem has 10 priority levels, how many different problems can be formulated if sensitivity analysis is used?

4.2 What is the meaning of an artificial variable in an optimal LGP solution basis?

4.3 Can we solve an LGP problem if one or more goal constraints have a negative right-hand-side value?

4.4 Under what conditions do we know we have an optimal solution when using the LGP solution procedure presented in this chapter?

4.5 Under what conditions do we know we have an optimal integer solution when using the branch-and-bound technique presented in this chapter?

4.6 Solve the following LGP problem using the LGP solution procedure:

$$\text{Minimize:} \quad Z = d_1^- + d_2^+ + d_3^-$$
$$\text{subject to:} \quad x_1 + 2x_2 + d_1^- - d_1^+ = 100$$
$$x_1 \qquad\quad + d_2^- - d_2^+ = 50$$
$$x_2 + d_3^- - d_3^+ = 25$$
$$\text{and} \quad x_j, d_i^-, d_i^+ \geq 0$$

4.7 Solve the following LGP problem using the LGP solution procedure:

$$\text{Minimize:} \quad Z = P_1(d_1^+) + P_2(d_2^-) + P_3(d_3^-) + P_4(d_4^-)$$
$$\text{subject to:} \quad 2x_1 + x_2 - d_1^+ \qquad\quad = 20$$
$$x_1 \qquad\quad + d_2^- = 5$$
$$x_2 \quad + d_3^- = 10$$
$$8x_1 + 3x_2 \qquad + d_4^- = 100$$
$$\text{and} \quad x_j, d_i^-, d_i^+ \geq 0$$

4.8 Solve the following LGP problem using the LGP solution procedure:

$$\text{Minimize:} \quad Z = P_1(d_1^- + d_2^-) + P_2(d_3^+) + P_4(d_4^+)$$
$$\text{subject to:} \quad x_1 \qquad\quad + d_1^- - d_1^+ = 4$$
$$x_2 + d_2^- - d_2^+ = 6$$
$$x_1 + x_2 + d_3^- - d_3^+ = 10$$
$$4x_1 + 2x_2 + d_4^- - d_4^+ = 50$$
$$\text{and} \quad x_j, d_i^-, d_i^+ \geq 0$$

4.9 Solve the following LGP problem using the LGP solution procedure:

Minimize: $Z = P_1 d_1^+ + 2P_2 d_2^- + P_2 d_3^- + P_2 d_4^- + P_3 d_5^+$

subject to:

$$800x_1 + 400x_2 + 500x_3 + d_1^- - d_1^+ = 8000$$
$$x_1 \qquad\qquad\qquad + d_2^- - d_2^+ = 3$$
$$x_2 \qquad\qquad + d_3^- - d_3^+ = 4$$
$$x_3 + d_4^- - d_4^+ = 2$$
$$x_1 + x_2 + x_3 + d_5^- - d_5^+ = 14$$

and $\qquad x_j,\, d_i^-,\, d_i^+ \geq 0$

4.10 Solve the following LGP problem using the LGP solution procedure:

Minimize: $Z = 3P_1(d_1^-) + P_1(d_2^-) + P_2(d_3^-) + P_3(d_3^+)$

subject to:

$$x_1 \qquad + d_1^- \qquad\qquad = 20$$
$$x_2 + d_2^- \qquad\qquad = 40$$
$$4x_1 + 2x_2 + d_3^- - d_3^+ = 120$$

and $\qquad x_j,\, d_i^-,\, d_i^+ \geq 0$

4.11 Solve the following LGP problem using the LGP solution procedure:

Minimize: $Z = P_1 d_1^+ + P_2 d_2^- + P_3 d_3^+ + P_4(d_4^+ + d_4^-)$

subject to:

$$0.5x_1 + 0.25x_2 \qquad\qquad - d_1^+ = 480$$
$$x_1 \qquad\qquad + d_2^- \qquad = 900$$
$$x_1 + x_2 + d_3^- - d_3^+ = 1{,}400$$
$$25x_1 + 125x_2 + d_4^- - d_4^+ = 216{,}000$$

and $\qquad x_j,\, d_i^-,\, d_i^+ \geq 0$

4.12 Solve the following LGP problem using the branch-and-bound techniques for an all integer solution.

Minimize: $Z = P_1 d_1^- + P_2(d_2^- + d_3^-)$

subject to:

$$4x_1 + 20x_2 \qquad + d_1^- = 100$$
$$x_1 + 10x_2 \qquad + d_2^- = 20$$
$$x_1 \qquad\qquad + d_3^- = 2$$

and $\qquad x_j \geq$ and all integer

$\qquad d_i^-,\, d_i^+ \geq 0$

4.13 Solve the following LGP problem using the LGP solution procedure:

Minimize: $Z = P_1 d_1^+ + 2P_2(d_2^+ + d_2^-) + P_2(d_3^+ + d_3^- + d_4^+ + d_4^-) + P_3 d_5^+$

subject to:
$$1.00x_1 + 1.30x_2 + 1.15x_3 + d_1^- - d_1^+ = 500$$
$$x_1 \qquad\qquad\qquad + d_2^- - d_2^+ = 220$$
$$x_2 \qquad\qquad + d_3^- - d_3^+ = 150$$
$$x_3 + d_4^- - d_4^+ = 75$$
$$x_1 + \quad x_2 + \quad x_3 + d_5^- - d_5^+ = 420$$

and $\qquad x_j, d_i^-, d_i^+ \geqslant 0$

4.14 Solve the following LGP problem using the LGP solution procedure.

Minimize: $Z = P_1d_1^- + P_2d_2^- + P_3d_3^+ + P_4d_4^- + P_5d_5^- + P_6d_6^-$

subject to:
$$4x_1 + 4x_2 + 4x_3 + d_1^- - d_1^+ = \quad 40$$
$$4x_1 + 5x_2 + 6x_3 + d_2^- - d_2^+ = 6000$$
$$4x_1 + 4x_2 + 4x_3 + d_3^- - d_3^+ = \quad 60$$
$$x_1 \qquad\qquad\qquad + d_4^- - d_4^+ = \quad 60$$
$$x_2 \qquad\qquad + d_5^- - d_5^+ = \quad 20$$
$$x_3 + d_6^- - d_6^+ = \quad 90$$

and $\qquad x_j, d_i^-, d_i^+ \geqslant 0$

4.15 Three people must be assigned to three jobs. The hourly cost of each of the three people to do each of the three jobs is given below:

	Job		
Person	A	B	C
I	56	89	85
II	101	88	240
III	110	91	65

Each person can be assigned to only one job. Each person must be assigned a different job. Beyond these assignment conditions, you must make the job assignment with the least possible cost. Formulate this problem as a zero-one LGP problem and solve for the optimal assignment schedule.

5

Computer
Based
Solutions

■ 5.1 ■ Chapter Overview

In this chapter two computer programs are described as aids in solving LGP problems. The procedures for coding LGP problem parameters into the computer programs are also presented. To illustrate how the computer programs are used, sample problems are analyzed.

■ 5.2 ■ Background Information

Access to computers increases each year. There are "macro," "mini," and "micro" computer systems, each with their own unique programming capabilities. In most cases, computer languages are interchangeable between the various computer systems. Unfortunately, software (i.e., computer programs) are not always interchangeable.

To insure that students using this book will have access to a computer program that can solve LGP problems, two computer programs are provided in the appendices of this book. The first program, written in FORTRAN, can be used on macro (i.e., mainframe) or mini computer systems. We will refer to this as the LGP "macro" computer system program. The second program, written in BASIC, is designed to be used on a personal or micro computer system. We will refer to this as the LGP "micro" computer system program.

In order to successfully use the computer programs described in this chapter, certain computer system prerequisites and computer limitations should be understood. There may be additional prerequisites and limitations beyond those discussed here due to the uniqueness of the computer facilities utilized. Students are encouraged to check with their instructor or computer center manager if unusual output is generated.

■ *Student and Computer System Prerequisites*

The LGP macro computer program presented in Appendix A of this book is a FORTRAN program capable of being interpreted by any standard FORTRAN compiler. The program requires an interactive computer-based system. (Students may, with minor alterations, change the program to be utilized on a computer system with a deck or batch entry mode. Such alterations in the program are beyond the scope of this book.) Students must be familiar with sufficient interactive computer system commands to enter and exit the computer system, enter the LGP program in their computer library (if necessary), create input data files, and place the files into the LGP program for processing. These computer system commands are usually made available at any computer center. If the LGP macro program has already been placed in the computer system, only the LGP problem coding procedure is necessary to input the problem parameters for solution purposes. This coding procedure is presented in Section 5.3.

The LGP micro computer program in Appendix B of this book is a BASIC computer program. It has been specifically written in Applesoft BASIC for an Apple II + computer system. The micro computer system should have at least a 48K memory with a DOS 3.3 (i.e., Disk Operating System) and an EPSON MX-80 printer. Students should be familiar with micro computer system terminology and equipment usage. The LGP micro computer program is set up to use data files or direct data entry. The coding procedure for direct entry problems requires the user to respond to a series of questions. This coding procedure is presented in Section 5.5.

■ *Computer Program Limitations*

The LGP macro computer program has limitations on the size of the problems it can solve. The parameter limits dimensioned in the code are 150 goal constraints, 150 decision variables and 10 preemptive priority levels. One desirable feature about the program, though, is it creates all necessary artificial deviational variables and an artificial priority level when necessary.

The LGP macro computer program is based on the same solution procedure presented in Chapter 4, but has one minor difference: the initial solution requires the basic variables to be d_i^- instead of d_i^+. This does not necessitate any special formulation or solution considerations.

One final limitation of the LGP macro computer program is that it does not provide the solution tableaus. It does state the number of iterations required to reach a solution and a complete summary of the optimal values of the decision variables and deviational variables as well as goal achievement information.

The LGP micro computer program has limitations on the size of the problems it can solve. The parameter limits in the code are approximately 35 goal constraints, 10 decision variables and 9 priorities. Users should be aware that large problems may consume a great deal of computer time.

This program, like the macro program, creates all necessary artificial deviational variables. Unfortunately, the program requires the user to place any artificial variables they add to the model at P_1 instead of P_0. This requires a shifting of the other priorities for any problem requiring an artificial deviational variable.

The LGP micro computer program is similar to the LGP macro program in that the initial solution requires the basic variables to be d_i^- instead of d_i^+. This means that each constraint that does not have a d_i^- variable must be given one, and this artificial deviational variable will be placed at P_1.

The LGP micro computer program does not provide all of the solution tableaus, but does allow users to specify the final tableau, if desired, as well as providing the complete optimal solution values and goal information.

One final limitation of the LGP micro computer program is that it is limited in its present form to an Apple computer system. Users familiar with IBM and other micro computer system languages should recognize the ease with which conversion to another computer system language is possible. The BASIC computer language in which the LGP micro computer program is written is fairly universal and permits easy conversion between alternative micro computer systems.

■ 5.3 ■ Macro Computer Program Coding Procedure

The coding procedure for the LGP macro computer program requires seven types of parameter information to be placed in a data file. The data is in a free format style (skip spaces between parameters when placed on the same line), but all values should be left-hand-justified. Unless otherwise directed, each piece of data should be placed on a separate line. The seven types of input parameter information and format specifications are as follows:

1. *number of goal constraints*
2. *number of decision variables*

3. *number of priority levels*

4. *sign symbol:* This indicates the direction of acceptable deviation in each of the goal constraints in the problem. More than one sign symbol may be placed on the same line. The sign symbols to choose from are as follows:

If goal constraints have	Then use this symbol
d_i^- and d_i^+	'B'
only d_i^-	'L'
only d_i^+	'G'
artificial d_i^-	'E'

5. *sign symbol and location of deviation variables:* (That is, the deviational variables in the objective function.) The format for each of the deviational variables requires four items: sign symbol (either 'POS' for a d_i^+ in the objective function or 'NEG' for a d_i^-), the goal constraint row number for the deviational variable, the preemptive priority level number, and the differentiating weight. When all of the information has been entered, a data ending signal must be entered. It will always be stated as: 'END' 0 0 0.

6. *technological coefficients:* The format for each technological coefficient (excluding zero values) is as follows: goal constraint row number, decision variable column number, and the technological coefficient value. Once the technological coefficients are all entered, an ending signal must be entered. It will always be stated: 0 0 0.

7. *right-hand-side values:* These values are entered in row order, separated by spaces.

This information completely describes the LGP problem to the macro computer program. By accessing the LGP macro program and placing this data file into it, a solution will be generated. To illustrate the LGP macro computer program and coding procedure, the next section uses the program to solve the Swifter Trucking Company problem that was presented in Section 3.3.

■ 5.4 ■ Application of
Macro Computer System Program

The Swifter Trucking Company LGP problem formulation can be restated as follows:

Minimize: $Z = 1.1P_1 (d_5^- + d_5^+) + P_1(d_1^- + d_1^+ + d_2^- + d_2^+ + d_3^- + d_3^+ + d_4^- + d_4^+ + d_6^- + d_6^+ + d_7^- + d_7^+ + d_8^- + d_8^+) + P_2d_9^+ + P_3(d_{10}^- + d_{10}^+) + P_4d_{11}^+$

$$\text{subject to: } x_1 + x_2 + x_3 + x_4 + x_5 + d_1^- - d_1^+ = 6$$
$$x_6 + x_7 + x_8 + x_9 + x_{10} + d_2^- - d_2^+ = 12$$
$$x_{11} + x_{12} + x_{13} + x_{14} + x_{15} + d_3^- - d_3^+ = 12$$
$$x_1 + x_6 + x_{11} + d_4^- - d_4^+ = 12$$
$$x_2 + x_7 + x_{12} + d_5^- - d_5^+ = 6$$
$$x_3 + x_8 + x_{13} + d_6^- - d_6^+ = 4$$
$$x_4 + x_9 + x_{14} + d_7^- - d_7^+ = 2$$
$$x_5 + x_{10} + x_{15} + d_8^- - d_8^+ = 6$$
$$x_2 \qquad - d_9^+ = 0$$
$$x_6 - x_8 + d_{10}^- - d_{10}^+ = 0$$
$$100x_1 + \cdots + 450\, x_{15} \qquad - d_{11}^+ = 0$$

and
$$x_j,\, d_i^-,\, d_i^+ \geq 0$$

To obtain the solution to this problem, its parameters are placed into a data file. Figure 5.1 contains the seven types of information placed in accordance with the LGP computer program format specifications. We then use the LGP macro computer program and this data file to solve the LGP problem. The output of the solution is presented in Figure 5.2. As can be seen, it took 14 iterations to solve the problem. The decision variables are listed by number and these optimal values are listed to the right of each variable number. In 5.2, the "Analysis of Deviations From Goals" section of the output defines, by goal constraint, the positive and negative deviation from the original right-hand-side values. The "Analysis of the Objective Function" section of the output defines goal achievement by priority level.

Figure 5.1 Parameter Input Data for Swifter Trucking Company Problem

```
11
15
4
'B' 'B' 'B' 'B' 'B' 'B' 'B' 'B' 'G' 'B' 'G'
'NEG' 5 1 1.1
'POS' 5 1 1.1
'NEG' 1 1 1
'POS' 1 1 1
'NEG' 2 1 1
'POS' 2 1 1
'NEG' 3 1 1
'POS' 3 1 1
'NEG' 4 1 1
'POS' 4 1 1
'NEG' 6 1 1
'POS' 6 1 1
```

```
'NEG'  7  1  1
'POS'  7  1  1
'NEG'  8  1  1
'POS'  8  1  1
'POS'  9  2  1
'NEG' 10  3  1
'POS' 10  3  1
'POS' 11  4  1
'END'  0  0  0
 1  1  1
 1  2  1
 1  3  1
 1  4  1
 1  5  1
 2  6  1
 2  7  1
 2  8  1
 2  9  1
 2 10  1
 3 11  1
 3 12  1
 3 13  1
 3 14  1
 3 15  1
 4  1  1
 4  6  1
 4 11  1
 5  2  1
 5  7  1
 5 12  1
 6  3  1
 6  8  1
 6 13  1
 7  4  1
 7  9  1
 7 14  1
 8  5  1
 8 10  1
 8 15  1
 9  2  1
10  6  1
10  8  -1
11  1  100
11  2  275
11  3  800
11  4  625
11  5  175
11  6  225
```

```
11  7  200
11  8  300
11  9  500
11  10  675
11  11  700
11  12  600
11  13  250
11  14  150
11  15  450
0  0  0
6  12  12  12  6  4  2  6  0  0  0
```

Figure 5.2   Output of Solution for Swifter Trucking Company Problem

14 ITERATIONS
DECISION VARIABLES

VARIABLE	VALUE
1	6.00000
2	0.00000
3	0.00000
4	0.00000
5	0.00000
6	3.00000
7	6.00000
8	3.00000
9	0.00000
10	0.00000
11	3.00000
12	0.00000
13	1.00000
14	2.00000
15	6.00000

ANALYSIS OF DEVIATIONS FROM GOALS

ROW	RHS-VALUE	POSITIVE DEVIATION	NEGATIVE DEVIATION
1	6.00000	0.00000	0.00000
2	12.00000	0.00000	0.00000
3	12.00000	0.00000	0.00000
4	12.00000	0.00000	0.00000
5	6.00000	0.00000	0.00000
6	4.00000	0.00000	0.00000
7	2.00000	0.00000	0.00000

8	6.00000	0.00000	0.00000
9	0.00000	0.00000	0.00000
10	0.00000	0.00000	0.00000
11	0.00000	8725.00000	0.00000

ANALYSIS OF THE OBJECTIVE FUNCTION

PRIORITY	UNDERACHIEVEMENT
4	8725.00000
3	0.00000
2	0.00000
1	0.00000
ARTIFICIAL	0.00000

It is interesting to note that an artificial priority level was created for this problem. This was necessary because goal constraints 9 and 11 did not have d_i^- variables in the problem formulation, and as stated in Section 5.2, "Computer Program Limitations," each goal constraint must have a negative deviational variable for an initial solution.

The use of the LGP macro computer program can save students a great deal of computation time if they have a macro or mini computer system available. Not everyone does have access to a macro or mini computer system. An increasing number of students do have access to micro computers. In Appendix B, an LGP micro computer program is presented. The coding procedure for this program is presented in Section 5.5.

■ 5.5 ■ Micro Computer Program Coding Procedure

The coding procedure for the LGP micro computer program listed in Appendix B involves activating the computer hardware and accessing the diskette containing the LGP micro computer program. (Students are expected to know how to enter the BASIC program listed in Appendix B onto a diskette.) Once the computer hardware and LGP program are activated, the user will immediately be asked a series of questions. The different types of questions a user may be asked are as follows:

1. *Do you want instruction?* If an *N* is typed in, the answer is no and the next question is asked. If a *Y* is typed in, the answer is yes and a brief set of data entry information is provided.

2. *Is your problem already on file?* If an *N* is typed in, the computer will not

look for a data file and assumes the user will use a direct entry mode for model parameters. If a Y is typed in, the computer will ask for data entry file information for a data file entry mode.

3. *Name your problem.* Users may use several characters to label the LGP problem they are working on.

4. *Number of unknowns.* The number of decision variables in the LGP model should be listed.

5. *Want to name variables?* If an N is typed in, the computer assigns the decision variables as x_j. If a Y is typed in, the user may label each decision variable with a term or word.

6. *Number of constraints.* The number of goal constraints in the LGP model should be listed.

7. *No. of deviational variables.* The number of negative deviational variables as formulated in the LGP model should be listed. All artificial d^- variables should be included.

8. *Number of priorities.* The number of priorities, including an additional one if an artificial variable is needed, should be listed.

9. *Type in number of variables which appear in equation (no.) or A for (A)ll.* This statement requires the user to identify the number of decision variables that appear in each goal constraint, one constraint at a time. If an A is typed in, the program assumes all decision variables are in the goal constraint. Otherwise the number of decision variables in each constraint should be listed.

10. *Enter value of x_j?* The technological coefficient for x_j should be entered.

11. *Enter subscript of unknown.* The subscript of the decision variable in the goal constraint that the user has already identified should be listed.

12. *Is pos. dev. var. allowed in equation (no.)?* If an N is typed in, the program assumes the goal constraint does not permit positive deviation from the right-hand-side value. If a Y is typed in, the program assumes the goal constraint permits positive deviation from the right-hand-side value.

13. *RHS for equation (no.)?* The right-hand-side value for the goal constraint that the user has already identified should be listed.

14. *Equation (no.) reads . . . Is it right?* The user has a chance here to correct the goal constraint entered if need be. If an N is typed in, corrections can be entered. If a Y is typed in, the computer assumes the goal constraint is correct.

15. *Priority associated with D_i?* The priority number attached to specific d_i^+ or d_i^- variables should be listed.

16. *Weight for the dev. var.* The differential weight attached to a specific deviational variable should be listed.

121

17. *Do you want printout?* If an N is typed in, the printer will not type out the solution. If a Y is typed in, the printer will type out the LGP solution.

18. *Including tableau?* If an N is typed in, the final tableau will not be printed out. If a Y is typed in, the final tableau will be typed out.

The answers to these questions permit the user to enter the LGP problem parameters into the computer and allow the LGP micro computer program to solve the problem. To illustrate how a user should answer these questions and how a problem is correctly entered, let's solve the Florance Manufacturing Company problem presented in Section 3.3.

■ 5.6 ■ Application
of Micro Computer
System Program

The Florance Manufacturing Company problem formulation can be restated as follows:

$$\text{Minimize:} \quad Z = P_1 d_1^+ + P_2(d_2^- + d_3^-) + P_3(d_2^+ + d_3^+) + P_4 d_4^+$$
$$\text{subject to:} \quad 3x_1 + 3x_2 + d_1^- - d_1^+ = 120$$
$$x_1 \quad\quad + d_2^- - d_2^+ = 10$$
$$x_2 + d_3^- - d_3^+ = 15$$
$$x_1 \quad\quad\quad\quad - d_4^+ = 5$$
$$\text{and} \quad\quad x_j, d_i^-, d_i^+ \geq 0$$

Before entering this problem into the computer, students should note that the fourth constraint does not have a d_4^- variable. As indicated earlier in this chapter, the computer program requires each goal constraint to have a negative deviational variable. To accommodate the program, an artificial deviational variable will be added. This variable will have to be placed at P_1 and so will necessitate the shifting of other deviational variables in the objective function. The new objective function for data entry purposes is as follows:

$$\text{Minimize:} \ Z = P_1 d_4^- + P_2 d_1^+ + P_3(d_2^- + d_3^-) + P_4(d_2^+ + d_3^+) + P_5 d_4^+$$

This adjustment is the only type of adjustment needed to enter data into the LGP micro computer program. We are now ready to access the program and start entering the problem parameters. The iterative questions and answers required to enter the Florance Manufacturing Company problem are presented in Figure 5.3. The solution provided by the LGP micro computer program is presented in Figure 5.4.

The LGP micro computer program's major advantage over the LGP macro

Figure 5.3 Input Data for Florance Manufacturing Company Problem

DO YOU WANT INSTRUCTIONS? N

IS YOUR PROBLEM ALREADY ON FILE? N

NAME YOUR PROBLEM. SCHNIEDERJANS EXAMPLE
READY TO ENTER DATA

NUMBER OF UNKNOWNS 2

WANT TO NAME VARIABLES? N

REMEMBER ONLY EQUATIONS WITH
DECISION VARIABLES COUNT IN
ANSWERING NEXT QUESTION.
NUMBER OF CONSTRAINTS 4

NO. OF DEVIATIONAL VARIABLES? 4

NUMBER OF PRIORITIES 5

IF ONLY 3 OR 4 UNKNOWNS IN PROBLEM
ANSWER NEXT QUESTION WITH 'A'.
IT WILL BE FASTER TO ENTER ALL.

TYPE IN NUMBER OF VARIABLES
WHICH APPEAR IN EQUATION 1
OR A FOR (A)LL. A
ENTER VALUE OF X1 ?3
ENTER VALUE OF X2 ?3

IS POS. DEV. VAR. ALLOWED IN
EQUATION 1?Y
RHS FOR EQUATION 1 ?120

EQUATION 1 READS:

$3 \times 1 + 3 \times 2 + D1 - - D1 + = 120$
IS IT RIGHT??Y
IF ONLY 3 OR 4 UNKNOWNS IN PROBLEM
ANSWER NEXT QUESTION WITH 'A'.
IT WILL BE FASTER TO ENTER ALL.

TYPE IN NUMBER OF VARIABLES
WHICH APPEAR IN EQUATION 2'
OR A FOR (A)LL. 1
ENTER SUBSCRIPT OF UNKNOWN 1
IN EQUATION 2 ?1
ENTER VALUE OF X1 ?1

IS POS. DEV. VAR. ALLOWED IN
EQUATION 2 ?Y
RHS FOR EQUATION 2 ?10

EQUATION 2 READS:

$1 \times 1 + 0 \times 2 + D2- - D2+ = 10$
IS IT RIGHT??Y
IF ONLY 3 OR 4 UNKNOWNS IN PROBLEM
ANSWER NEXT QUESTION WITH 'A'.
IT WILL BE FASTER TO ENTER ALL.

TYPE IN NUMBER OF VARIABLES
WHICH APPEAR IN EQUATION 3
OR A FOR (A)LL. 1
ENTER SUBSCRIPT OF UNKNOWN 1
IN EQUATION 3 ?2
ENTER VALUE OF $\times 2$?1

IS POS. DEV. VAR. ALLOWED IN
EQUATION 3 ?Y
RHS FOR EQUATION 3 ?15

EQUATION 3 READS:

$0 \times 1 + 1 \times 2 + D3- - D3+ = 15$
IS IT RIGHT??Y
IF ONLY 3 OR 4 UNKNOWNS IN PROBLEM
ANSWER NEXT QUESTION WITH 'A'.
IT WILL BE FASTER TO ENTER ALL.

TYPE IN NUMBER OF VARIABLES
WHICH APPEAR IN EQUATION 4
OR A FOR (A)LL. 1
ENTER SUBSCRIPT OF UNKNOWN 1
IN EQUATION 4 ?1
ENTER VALUE OF $\times 1$?1

IS POS. DEV. VAR. ALLOWED IN
EQUATION 4 ?Y
RHS FOR EQUATION 4 ?5

EQUATION 4 READS:

$1 \times 1 + 0 \times 2 + D4- - D4+ = 5$
IS IT RIGHT??Y

PRIORITY ASSOCIATED WITH D1 − ?0
WEIGHT FOR THE DEV.VAR.0
PRIORITY ASSOCIATED WITH D2 − ?3
WEIGHT FOR THE DEV.VAR.1
PRIORITY ASSOCIATED WITH D3 − ?3
WEIGHT FOR THE DEV.VAR.1
PRIORITY ASSOCIATED WITH D4 − ?1
WEIGHT FOR THE DEV.VAR.1
PRIORITY ASSOCIATED WITH D1 + ?2
WEIGHT FOR THE DEV.VAR.1

PRIORITY ASSOCIATED WITH D2 + ?4
WEIGHT FOR THE DEV.VAR.1

PRIORITY ASSOCIATED WITH D3 + ?4
WEIGHT FOR THE DEV.VAR.1

PRIORITY ASSOCIATED WITH D4 + ?5
WEIGHT FOR THE DEV.VAR.1

DO YOU WANT PRINTOUT? Y

INCLUDING TABLEAU? N

Figure 5.4 Output of Solution for Florance Manufacturing Company

SCHNIEDERJANS EXAMPLE

SOLUTION VARIABLES ARE:

D1 −	45
D4 +	5
X2	15
X1	10

UNACHIEVED GOALS ARE:

P5	5

computer program is ease of data entry. The LGP macro computer program's major advantage over the LGP micro computer program is its ability to solve larger scale problems.

Having explained the coding procedures for model parameters and illustrated the input and output generated by both LGP computer programs, students are encouraged to practice using both computer programs. Many LGP problems (and their solutions for checking purposes) are available in the prior research studies listed in the bibliography in Section 1.3.

■ 5.7 ■ Summary

Presented in this chapter are two computer programs for solving LGP problems. Both a macro and micro computer system program are provided. Coding procedures, limitations, and illustrative examples of their use are also presented.

Students may wish to modify the LGP macro and micro computer programs to accommodate larger sized problems. Such adjustments can be easily made, but care should be taken not to expand the program beyond the students' computer system capability. Also, remember that programs requiring a great deal of computer core or space will usually require a longer turnaround input/output time. The time saved in computational effort by using these computer programs should be devoted to problem formulation and solution analysis. The case problems presented in Part II of this text are designed to help students develop skill in LGP problem formulation and solution analysis.

KEY VOCABULARY

Coding procedure

Computer program limitations

Data file

Macro computer system

Micro computer system

Sign symbol

CHAPTER QUESTIONS

5.1   Solve the Ollie Advertising Company problem presented in Section 3.3, using the micro computer system program.

5.2.   Solve the zero-one problem presented in Section 4.5, "Application," using the macro computer system program.

5.3   Solve Chapter Question 4.6 using the micro computer system program.

5.4   Solve Chapter Question 4.7 using the micro computer system program.

5.5   Solve Chapter Question 4.8 using the micro computer system program.

5.6   Solve Chapter Question 4.9 using the micro computer system program.

5.7   Solve Chapter Question 4.10 using the micro computer system program.

5.8   Solve Chapter Question 4.12 using the micro computer system program.

5.9   Solve Chapter Question 4.13 using the micro computer system program.

5.10   Solve Chapter Question 4.11 using the macro computer system program.

5.11   Solve Chapter Question 4.12 using the macro computer system program.

5.12   Solve Chapter Question 4.13 using the macro computer system program.

5.13   Solve Chapter Question 4.14 using the macro computer system program.

5.14   Solve Chapter Question 4.15 using the macro computer system program.

5.15   Hard Press Records (HPR), a private company, prints two types of records: albums and extended play 45's (E.P.s). The total cost for manufacturing one album is $6.25 and $2.75 for one E.P. The President of HPR has determined that the selling price of an album is $8.00 and one E.P. is $3.50. His first goal is to make $4,000 profit a week. His second goal is to meet sales; selling albums is twice as important as selling E.P.s. He wants to sell 2,000 albums and 900 E.P.s per week. Formulate and solve this LGP problem using the macro computer program.

II
CASES

■ Foreward

Each chapter in Part II contains a case *problem, requiring an LGP model for-mulation, solution or post-solution analysis, a set of* chapter questions *(that will help guide students in resolving the case problem), and a set of* selected references *(from which the case problem was developed and may assist students in under-standing the case). The names of people and places in the cases have been altered or contrived. The reader is encouraged to research the selected references in answering the questions at the end of each case.*

6
Northern Florida Data Processing Division

In December of 1982, Cathy Jensen, the Chief Accounting Director of the northern government region of the state of Florida, invited two Florida state cost accountants, Cindy LeGrande and Joye Hern, to advise her on a cost accounting problem. As Chief Accounting Director, Ms. Jensen is responsible for resolving any accounting problems the state government of Florida has in any of its cities in the northern region. Cindy and Joye are cost accountants who work under the Chief Accounting Director in northern Florida.

After meeting Cindy and Joye, Cathy started describing the cost accounting problem she was facing.

CATHY JENSEN: As you know, priorities for the allocation of public funds to projects are set by such groups as elected officials, public advisory groups and also by department and agency managers. One type of division manager in my local government organization is a Data Processing Manager. John Anderson is currently our Data Processing Manager. He has a set of unique problems in setting goals and priorities for his agency. This manager's decisions concern rates for data processing resources to be charged to other agencies also under my jurisdiction. As you both know, we here in the northern region, and throughout the state, have encountered problems in budgeting and rate setting for our small to medium sized data processing divisions. The complexities compound further when we address the unique qualities of the problem due to the government user agency budget restrictions and government related restrictions on the D.P. (i.e., Data Processing) division itself. What I need is a model which can be used in a local government data processing division to set its rates for the computer and personnel resources that are used by other agencies in the government entity. I would also like you both to develop a presentation, when you have prepared the model, to sell the model and its use to my entire staff. The presentation should include a background description of the problems faced by our data processing divisions in this environment, with emphasis on the highly interdependent relationship between the data processing division budget, user budgets, and the rates themselves. I am particularly interested in all model assumptions you have to make in developing your model. It is easier for all of us to believe in the output of the model if the model is validly based on agreeable and realistic assumptions. The better your presentation, the easier its results will be implemented.

CINDY LEGRANDE AND JOYE HERN: We'll do the best we can.

In March of 1983, Cindy and Joye had prepared the presentation of their user rate model. In late March of 1983, the entire data processing staff of the northern region of the state of Florida, several state cost accountants and Cathy Jensen were present.

CINDY LEGRANDE AND JOYE HERN: To aid in your understanding of our user pricing model, and consistent with Ms. Jensen's request, we have divided our presentation into three parts: *Problem Background*—which describes our perceptions of the problems you face in pricing user services; *Pricing Model Description*—which includes model symbol definitions, the model formulation and an explanation of the model's elements; and *Implementation*—which expresses our ideas on how you might use the model we have developed.

Problem Background: A local government data processing division has many objectives and constraints not seen by data processing managers in private industry. The division is expected to provide information processing services to any and all public agencies within the structure of the local government institution. These services must be provided using limited resources of personnel (programmers, project leaders, etc.) and equipment (CPU time, storage space, etc.). In addition, for budgetary purposes and for evaluation, the data processing division must act as a cost center for the rest of the government agencies, expending funds for production and recovering these funds through chargeback to the individual user agencies. A unique quality of a government data processing division is that revenue from the use of its resources must exactly balance the expenditures made. This must be taken into account when setting rates for these resources.

The budget process typically starts with the project leaders who work closely with each user agency, making a projection of the resource needs of the user in the coming fiscal year. These needs are listed in terms of hours of programmer time, CPU seconds of processor time, etc. The projection also includes an estimation of the cost of these needs based on current rates. Three types of activities are basically projected for each user agency: maintenance of existing systems, changes to existing systems due to policy change, and development projects.

Concurrent with these activities, the data processing manager prepares his own division budget, projecting future costs in personnel, equipment and even his own computer needs. These projections are revised when the user budgets are aggregated and a need for more capacity is seen.

Once the total expenditures for the division are known and the expected revenue producing activity is compiled, the rates for these activities must be set in order to recover an amount equal to the amount of other expenditures. For purposes of evaluation at one level lower, a restriction is made that programmer and analyst activity should recover application software development section expenditures and the computer activities should recover the operations section expenditures. To recover expenditures by supporting sections such as technical services and administration, they are allocated to both of the revenue sections according to standard cost allocation methods.

The problem that arises from this process is that once rates are set and applied back to the projected needs of each user agency, it may happen that the total cost of these needs exceeds the total amount available to that agency. In this case, the agency will attempt to reduce its needs by first cutting back on development projects, then putting off minor changes to the systems, and finally, if necessary, cutting back on its maintenance costs by eliminating unnecessary reports and other processing. This cutback by the user agency lowers the projected resource activity for the data processing division and results in a shortfall of funds. The choice faced by the data processing manager is to either cut back his own expenditures or to revise the rates based on the new projected activity. Each of these methods will result in revision in the user budgets again and a seemingly endless occillation begins.

Pricing Model Description: The model described here will, through goal programming, find the satisfying rates for three levels of programmers, a project leader, and five different types of revenue generating equipment. The model assumes that revenue is generated in two sections of the division, Application Development and Operations, and that all other section expenditures are allocated to these sections for recovery.

Symbols used in the description of the model are:

Symbol	Description
x_i	Decision variable where $i = 1, 2, \ldots 9$
d^-, d^+	Deviational variables
n_i	Number of units of decision variable x_i available
E_1, E_2, E_3	Division, Application Development and Operations expenditures

133

H_1, H_2	Total programmer and project leader hours
S	Expended total CPU seconds used
L	Expected total printer lines printed
C	Expected total cards read
T	Expected total number of reads to a tape
D	Expected total number of reads to a disk
U_j	Total user budget for user j where $j = 1,2, \ldots, J$
M_j	Total user budget for user j for maintenance
C_j	Total user budget for user j for changes
Q_{jk}	Total user budget for user j for project k where $k = 1,2, \ldots, K$
m_{ji}	Number of units at rate x_i needed for maintenance for user j
c_{ji}	Number of units at rate x_i needed for changes for user j
q_{jki}	Number of units at rate x_i needed for project k and for user j
w_{jk}	Differentiating weight for user j and project k

The decision variables used in the model are as follows:

Variable	Description
x_1	Rate for one hour of programmer I time in dollars
x_2	Rate for one hour of programmer II time in dollars
x_3	Rate for one hour of programmer III time in dollars
x_4	Rate for one hour of project leader time in dollars
x_5	Rate for one second of CPU time
x_6	Rate for one line printed on the printer
x_7	Rate for one card read on the card reader
x_8	Rate for one record read on a tape drive
x_9	Rate for one record read on a disk drive

The priorities used in the Model are as follows:

Priorities	Description
P_1	Total revenue from all variables must equal total expenditures for the division and sections
P_2	User budgets cannot be exceeded
P_3	Personnel resources should be fully utilized and overutilization should be avoided
P_4	Equipment resources should be fully utilized
P_5	Each user maintenance budget must not be exceeded
P_6	Each user changes budget must not be exceeded
P_7	Each user project budget must not be exceeded

134

■ Model Formulation

In order to achieve all of the goals described above within the constraints of the budget process, the following model is proposed for the setting of rates for a computer data processing division:

$$\text{Minimize: } Z = 2P_1(d_1^- + d_1^+) + P_1(d_2^- + d_2^+ + d_3^- + d_3^+) + P_2\sum_{j=1}^{J}d_j^+$$

$$+ 2P_3(d_4^- + d_5^-) + P_3(d_4^+ + d_5^+) + P_4(d_6^- + d_7^- + d_8^-$$

$$+ d_9^- + d_{10}^-) + P_5(\sum_{j=1}^{J}d_j^+) + P_6(\sum_{j=1}^{J}d_j^+ \; P_7(\sum_{k=1}^{K}\sum_{j=1}^{J}d_{jk}^+ w_{jk})$$

subject to:

$$\sum_{i=1}^{9} n_i x_i + d_1^- - d_1^+ = E_1 \qquad \textbf{(6.1)}$$

(Division expenditure)

$$\sum_{i=1}^{4} n_i x_i + d_2^- - d_2^+ = E_2 \qquad \textbf{(6.2)}$$

(Application expenditure)

$$\sum_{i=1}^{9} n_i x_i + d_3^- - d_3^+ = E_3 \qquad \textbf{(6.3)}$$

(Operations expenditure)

$$\sum_{i=1}^{3} E_2/4 \; x_i + d_4^- - d_4^+ = H_1 \qquad \textbf{(6.4)}$$

(Programmer hours)

$$E_2/4 \; x_4 + d_5^- - d_5^+ = H_2 \qquad \textbf{(6.5)}$$

(Project leader hours)

$$E_3/5 \; x_5 + d_6^- - d_6^+ = S \quad \text{(CPU seconds)} \qquad \textbf{(6.6)}$$

$$E_3/x_6 + d_7^- - d_7^+ = L \quad \text{(Printer)} \qquad \textbf{(6.7)}$$

$$E_3/x_7 + d_8^- - d_8^+ = C \quad \text{(Reader)} \qquad \textbf{(6.8)}$$

$$E_3/x_8 + d_9^- - d_9^+ = T \quad \text{(Tape)} \qquad \textbf{(6.9)}$$

$$E_3/2 \; x_9 + d_{10}^- - d_{10}^+ = D \quad \text{(Disk)} \qquad \textbf{(6.10)}$$

$$\sum_{j=1}^{J}\sum_{i=1}^{9} m_{ji} x_i + c_{ji} x_i + \sum_{k=1}^{K}(q_{jki}x_i) + d_j^- - d_j^+ = U_j \quad \text{(User Budget)} \qquad \textbf{(6.11)}$$

$$\sum_{j=1}^{J}\sum_{i=1}^{9} m_{ji}x_i + d_j^- - d_j^+ = M_j \qquad \textbf{(6.12)}$$

(Maintenance budget)

$$\sum_{j=1}^{J}\sum_{i=1}^{9} c_{ji}x_i + d_j^- - d_j^+ = C_j \quad \text{(Change budget)} \qquad \textbf{(6.13)}$$

$$\sum_{j=1}^{J}\sum_{k=1}^{K}\sum_{i=1}^{9} q_{jki}x_i + d_{jk}^- - d_{jk}^+ = Q_{jk} \quad \text{(Projects)} \qquad \textbf{(6.14)}$$

and $\qquad x_i, \; d_j^-, \; d_j^+ \geq 0$

135

■ Constraint Description

Equation 6.1 is the primary constraint for the model. It states, simply, that total revenues should equal total expenditures for the Division. The symbol E_1 denotes the total Division expenditures. The product $n_i x_i$ is the number of units available in the time period (e.g., 2,080 hours for programmers) for a resource times the rate for that resource. All nine rate variables are summed to equal total revenue. The weight attached to deviations from Division total expenditures is twice that of the applications and operations sections. Equations 6.2 and 6.3 are the same as Equation 6.1 and state that total revenue in each of the equations should equal the total expenditures for those sections.

Equations 6.4 and 6.5 are constraints necessary to fully utilize the available programmers without high deviations below or above the available hours. The expression $E_2/4 x_i$ represents the number of programmer hours necessary to recover one-fourth the section expenditures. The ratio $E_2/4 x_4$ in Equation 6.5 is the equivalent for project leaders. The number 4 in the denominator of each equation is merely the ratio of each type of employee to the total. For the purpose of our model, an equal number of each type is assumed.

Equations 6.6 through 6.10 are the equivalent constraints for each of the five equipment revenue charges: CPU seconds, Printer lines, Cards read, Tapes read, and Disks read. Each right-hand-side value is *not* the total available number of units based on the expected total activity for that equipment from historical data. In contrast to the programmer and project leader hours constraints, it is not important if the *actual* activity exceeds the *expected* activity.

Equation 6.11 is the constraint used to model each of the user agencies. There is one constraint per agency. The product of $m_{ji} x_i$ is the cost of the required number of units at rate x_i to maintain the systems for user j. The expression $c_{ji} x_i$ represents the cost of the required number of units at rate x_i to make prescribed changes to the existing systems for user j. The product of $q_{jki} x_i$ represents the cost of the required number of units at rate x_i to develop the system under project k.

Equations 6.12 and 6.13 use the same summation of costs idea as Equation 6.11, but broken down by maintenance and system change activity. There is one constraint equation for each user for both maintenance and change.

Equation 6.14 is the sum of the costs related to the activity need for project k, user j. There is one constraint for each project under every user agency. All three constraint groups restrict the model so that the individual parts of the total user budget are treated separately with different priorities in the objective function.

■ Objective Function

For the first priority, where it is desired that revenue equal expense, the positive and negative deviation variables are included in the objective function. Those for the total revenue constraint are weighted twice those for the section revenue constraints. The objective function factors for the user budget, maintenance budget, change budget and project budget include the positive deviation variables from each constraint for each user agency. For the project development constraints, there is one deviation variable per project. Each individual project variable has an equal weight associated with it under Priority 7. These weights would be assigned individually by either the user agency or a steering committee for new development projects.

The objective function for personnel capacity usage contains a deviation variable for both positive and negative deviations. The negative deviations are weighted twice the positive deviations since it is more important to fully utilize all the personnel time available. This weight was subjectively determined.

The equipment usage deviational variables in the objective function are all negative because it is necessary for the expected equipment activity to be reached since this is what the revenue from this area will be directly dependent on.

Implementation: When implemented in a Data Processing Division, such as in northern Florida, this model will serve two important functions. First, it will serve as a starting point for the basic rate-setting procedure that must accompany the annual budget process. The rates that are calculated in this manner will not necessarily be the best rates, but they will serve as close approximations that can be used in further cost analysis.

Secondly, if implemented in an online interactive mode, this computer mode can serve as an important decision support system for future decisions concerning the acquisition of additional capacity, both personnel and equipment. A computer run of the model with new capacity figures on the maximum programmer hours available or the greater expected activity in the processor, disk storage, etc., will give an indication of the effect on user budgets; specifically, the purchase of a new computer or the hiring of additional programmers and the effect on budget planning.

Finally, the main and most immediate benefit would be the reduction of the very long iterative process now necessary to set rates and balance the data processing budget with user budgets. The reduction in time and labor would justify the implementation of the model alone.

CHAPTER QUESTIONS

6.1 Did Cindy and Joye fully complete the assignment Cathy Jensen gave them? What, if anything, did they leave out of their presentation?

6.2 Is the model erroneous in any way? Critique any modeling formulation or logic errors.

6.3 Will this model pose any problems if we try to use it? That is, using the model as formulated, will there be any difficulties in coding the model parameters into a computer program? Will there be additional computation required to obtain the model parameters?

6.4 What additional information, beyond that discussed by Cindy and Joye in the Implementation Section of their presentation, is generated by this LGP pricing model? Describe in detail.

SELECTED REFERENCES

De, P.K.; Acharya, D.; and Sahu, K.C., "A Chance-Constrained Goal Programming Model for Capital Budgeting," *Journal of the Operational Research Society,* Vol. 33, No. 7, (July, 1982), pp. 635–638.

Killough, L.N., and Sounders, T.L., "A Goal Programming Model for Public Accounting Firms," *The Accounting Review,* Vol. 48, (April, 1973), pp. 268–279.

Lee, S.M., and Wilkins, S.J., "Computer Facility Centralization/Decentralization: A Multiobjective Analysis Model," *Computers and Operations Research,* Vol. 10, No. 1, (1983), pp. 29–40.

7

Bacon and Allyn Personal Investment Corporation

In September of 1982 the Bacon and Allyn Personal Investments Corporation (BAPIC) was incorporated. BAPIC consists of a small personal investment firm, owned and operated by Jill Bacon and Alexander Allyn. The firm specializes in financial planning advice to medium-income tax bracket people. After several months of operation, Jill and Alexander found themselves making the same types of decisions repeatedly for differing clients. Their routine went as follows:

1. Secure potential client and determine the amount of funds the client wants to invest.

2. Research potential investment opportunities and their projected yearly rate of return. (These opportunities sometimes varied as a function of the amount of funds the client was willing to invest. The projected yearly rate of return was obtained from published sources and intuitive judgment.)

3. Determine the client's investment goals. (This will include any client preferences for certain types of investment such as a short term or long term type investment and/or risk aversion.)

4. Prepare and present a proposal of an investment portfolio of the alternative investment opportunities.

Jill and Alexander felt that a model that could be used in their computer system might save some duplication of effort. What they were looking for was a model they could modify slightly for each client and use repeatedly to generate an optimal investment portfolio based on the individual client's investment preferences. They decided to build the model themselves.

To begin developing the model, they researched the literature to determine which type of optimization procedure to use to model their multi-objective portfolio-type problem. They decided LGP would best model the conflicting investment decision situation.

Jill and Alexander then researched their files to determine a "typical" or "composite" client. This "composite" client could then be used as a base upon which to develop a prototype model. Minor adjustments to the prototype model could be made in the future to model real clients. From their research they found their "composite" client worked at the Utility Company (i.e., a local water company), had a gross yearly salary of $25,000, and can invest $5,000 to establish an initial portfolio. Having created this hypothetical client, the next step in their routine was to research potential investment opportunities and their projected yearly rate of return. Based on salary and investment capabilities, the investment opportunities for this "composite" client are presented in Exhibit 7.1.

Exhibit 7.1 Investment Opportunities and Their Projected Yearly Rate of Return

Investment Opportunity	Projected Yearly Rate of Return	Decision Variable in LGP Model
Dollars invested in an IRA (Retirement)	47	x_1
Dollars invested in the Utility Company Retirement Plan (Retirement)	208	x_2
Dollars invested in the Utility Company Deferred Income Plan (Retirement)	45	x_3
Dollars invested in the Pioneer Fund (Mutual Funds)	8	x_4
Dollars invested in the Lidner Fund (Mutual Funds)	25	x_5
Dollars invested in Dreyfus Liquid Assets (Money Markets)	13	x_6
Dollars invested in Merrill Lynch Ready Assets (Money Markets)	14	x_7
Dollars invested in the City-County Credit Union (Savings Accounts)	10	x_8
Dollars invested in the First Federal Savings and Loan (Savings Accounts)	9	x_9
Dollars invested in the Utility Company for More Investment Club	14.4	x_{10}

In Exhibit 7.1 the IRA Utility Company Retirement Plan and Utility Company Deferred Income Plan are included in the analysis for the purpose of putting money away for retirement. The potential money initially being saved due to the tax break given for IRA's and Deferred Income plans are included in the return percentage. Jill and Alexander knew that a person in the 35% tax bracket plugging $1000 into an IRA will be $350 richer when income taxes are paid at the first of the following year. In the case of the IRA, the interest given (12%) plus the tax break (35%) shows a total return of 47% on the money placed in the IRA. The other extreme could be included too; reducing the projected rates of return by 35%, leaving an after-tax rate of return. In most cases, research revealed this amounts to very little. For example, reducing the 8% rate of return projected for the Pioneer Fund by 35% leaves an after-tax return of 5.2%. This will add up in the long run, but for the purpose of an initial investment portfolio it will be left out of the model. Also, for every dollar going into an IRA or a deferred income plan, the tax bracket of the individual will be lowered. Again, this only complicates the picture, so it will be left out of the model.

The third step in the investment portfolio routine was in determining the client goals. Based on the "composite" of clients Jill and Alexander worked with, they developed the following goals in order of their importance:

1. Fulfill the Retirement Plan requirements of investing not less than 1% and not more than 5% of an individual's gross salary. This is a condition in which the investor, who worked for the Utility Company, is eligible for inclusion in the retirement plan.

2. Fulfill the Utility Company For More Investment Club requirements of investing not less than $150 per year.

3. Fulfill the Utility Company For More Investment Club requirements of investing not more than 15% of the total amount invested by all club members, which at this time is $5,000.

4. The amount of money invested in mutual funds is desired to be 60% of that invested in the money market. The amount of money invested in savings accounts and the Utility Company Investment Club each are desired to be 20% of that invested in the money market.

5. The amount of money alloted for retirement should not be greater than 30% of the total money available.

6. The amount of money alloted for investments should not be less than 70% of the total money available.

7. Obtain the largest return on investment opportunities as possible.

8. Invest the full amount of available money.

Based on the goals, priorities in the LGP model could be established. Jill and

Alexander next needed to develop appropriate goal constraints. The constraints used in a portfolio analysis usually tend to be *structural, legal,* or *policy*. The amount of funds available is an example of structural constraint. Examples of legal constraints are the maximum amount of money allowed to be deposited in an IRA each year or an interval on the amount of money allowed to be invested in a company retirement plan. Also, the minimum investment requirement of mutual funds comes under this heading. Policy constraints involve individual preference. This includes the individual's investment guidelines, such as not having more than a certain percentage of money available to invest in a certain area.

Having defined the investment opportunities listed in Exhibit 7.1 as decision variables, and having defined the model's goals, Jill and Alexander developed their LGP model for the "composite" client. The LGP model is presented in Exhibit 7.2.

Exhibit 7.2 LGP Model for Composite Client

Minimize Z: $= P_1 d_1^+ + P_1 d_2^- + P_2 d_3^+ + P_3 d_4^- + P_3 d_5^-$
$$+ P_4 d_6^+ + P_4 d_6^- + P_4 d_7^+ + P_4 d_7^- + P_5 d_8^- + P_6 d_9^+ + P_7 d_{10}^+ +$$
$$P_8 d_{11}^-$$

subject to:

$$x_2 - d_1^+ = 150$$
$$x_2 + d_2^- = 1250$$
$$x_{10} - d_3^+ = 150$$
$$x_{10} + d_4^- = 750$$
$$x_4 + x_5 - .6x_6 - .6x_7 - d_5^+ + d_5^- = 0$$
$$-.2x_6 - .2x_7 + x_8 + x_9 - d_6^+ + d_6^- = 0$$
$$-.2x_6 - .2x_7 + x_{10} - d_7^+ + d_7^- = 0$$
$$x_1 + x_2 + x_3 + d_8^- = 1500$$
$$x_4 + x_5 + x_6 + x_7 + x_8 + x_9 + x_{10} - d_9^+ = 350$$
$$.47x_1 + 2.08x_2 + .45x_3 + .08x_4 + .25x_5 + .13x_6 + .14x_7 + .10x_8 +$$
$$.09x_9 + .144x_{10} - d_{10}^+ + d_{10}^- = M$$
$$x_1 + x_2 + x_3 + x_4 + x_5 + x_6 + x_7 + x_8 + x_9 + x_{10} + d_{11}^- = 5000$$

and

$$x_j, d_i^+, d_i^- \geq 0$$

CHAPTER QUESTIONS

7.1 Did Jill and Alexander correctly formulate the LGP problem? Make any changes in the model you feel necessary to correctly model the problem situation.

7.2 How is the model presented in Exhibit 7.2 useful to BAPIC? What elements in this LGP model may have to be changed to be useful for portfolio decisions concerning other clients?

7.3 Based on your changes in Question 7.1, what is the optimal investment portfolio for the composite client?

SELECTED REFERENCES

Caplin, D.A., and Kornbluth, J.S.H., "Multiobjective Investment Planning Under Certainty," *OMEGA,* Vol. 3, No. 4, (August, 1975), pp. 423–441.

Kumar, P.C.; Philippatos, G.C.; and Ezzell, J.R.," Goal Programming and the Selection of Portfolios by Dual-Purpose Funds," *The Journal of Finance,* Vol. 33, No. 1, (March, 1978), pp. 303–310.

Sealey, C.W., "Financial Planning with Multiple Objectives," *Financial Management,* Vol. 7, (Winter, 1978), pp. 17–23.

8
Texas
National Savings
Bank

In January 1983, Frederico Sanco, President of the Texaco National Savings Bank (TNSB) hired a consultant to advise him on bank asset-management planning. The consultant, Johnson Smith, had worked for TNSB several years and was currently working on his Ph.D. at a local university.

FREDERICO SANCO: As you know, Johnson, the business of making loans is one of the major concerns of a bank's management, especially with regard to profits, for these loans are where the majority of a bank's earnings come from. For this reason, banks are an ongoing concern because they expect to make future loans and to follow through on the ones they have committed themselves to. The effective management of a loan portfolio is critical to both the security and profitability of a bank due to the risk and return tradeoff involved. More volatile portfolios will usually generate higher returns, but banks must allow for a certain amount of security at the expense of part of this return. This is done through diversification.

Diversification of the loan portfolio as well as of the entire asset portfolio will give the highest maximum return at the highest possible security. What we are looking for is the best solution to a set of portfolio goals relative to certain risk restrictions placed on these goals.

The management of assets is another major concern of all banks. These assets, however, are not just the investment securities of the bank. They include the various types of loans, cash, and other accounts on the bank's balance sheet on the asset side. For this reason, asset-management is not just portfolio management as many bankers think. Many decisions made with regard to the investment portfolio are probably not optimal if this portfolio is regarded as a separate area of concern. We call this investment portfolio "investment assets," used here to mean those assets which will be managed by the diversification of deposits.

Because of the implications of risks and return for loans as well as the misconceived ideas of a bank's assets, the management of a bank must look at the interactions that occur between the investment portfolio and the lending policy of the bank. This is necessary in order to obtain the best solution concerning appropriate investment action. In other words, asset-management—or the simultaneous planning of the entire asset side of the bank's balance sheet—should be a vital part of management's decision-making at a bank.

Johnson, we are hoping you can develop a model for us that will answer the following question:

Given TNSB's banking situation and its level of deposits and multiple conflicting goals, what diversification proportions of TNSB's assets will give the best solution consistent with the stated goals? The goals, in the order of their importance, are as follows:

1. Achieve a target level of 15% of total deposits in reserves and cash.

2. Achieve a target level of 65% of total deposits in total loans.

3. Achieve a target level of 20% of total deposits in investment securities (T-bills, long-term governments, municipal bonds).

4. Achieve a *minimum* rate of return on all investment assets of at least 12%.

5. Achieve a maximum total risk coefficient of 3 or lower. (Risk coefficient to be explained later.)

In the past we have hired consultants who developed models, derived answers and gave us a solution on a "take it or leave it" basis. This sometimes does not generate a successful or implementable solution for our purposes. Therefore, we want you not only to develop a model and derive a solution regarding our asset investment alternatives, but also to present a discussion on how the model was developed, all necessary assumptions and any comments you would like to share with us on the future use of the model. In this way we can better understand the limitations and usefulness of your model in our asset planning efforts.

JOHNSON SMITH: This model and the supportive presentation should only take about one week to develop. This assumes you will allow me to obtain all necessary data collection and an opportunity to talk with several other bank officers for data purposes. See you next week!

During the next week Smith talked with all of the remaining TNSB's officers. He polled their opinions on types of investment opportunities the bank could take advantage of as well as other real-world limitations that should be placed on an asset-management model. Based on these observations Johnson developed a model that he felt would satisfy Mr. Sanco. President Sanco called a meeting of all his bank officers to hear the results of Johnson's consulting efforts on the bank's behalf.

JOHNSON SMITH: The basic asset management question facing TNSB is: Given a certain level of deposits and multiple conflicting goals, what diversification proportions of these assets will give the best solution consistent with these goals? Given this question, the goals President Sanco stated, and many of the comments other bank officers mentioned, the first step was to derive the decision variables used in the model. The model variables and constraints are presented in Exhibit 8.1. The first necessary assumption is that total deposits are equal to total liabilities. In other words, the only liabilities that the bank has are in deposits. This leads to the next assumption and the foundation of the model. This key assumption is that the total amount of deposits is equal to the total amount which can be diversified into investment assets. It is then easy to see another assumption. This next assumption is that total bank capital must be equal to the buildings (i.e., bank premises) and other assets of the bank. Thus the problem can also be thought of as a balance sheet management problem. The premise of the balance sheet is that assets are equal to the liabilities plus equity (capital). It is implied then that the major assets of the bank are its loan portfolio and its investment portfolio. For simplicity, assets such as Federal Funds, buildings, equipment and other assets were ignored because it is felt they could be highly variable and dependent on the size of the bank, the market it serves and its overall objectives in the banking industry. The loan portfolio and the investment portfolio were selected along with reserves and cash due from banks. These represent the major assets of the bank and part of the reason for its profitable and secure existence.

Eight variables were defined on the basis of these assumptions. It was also necessary to include three variables representing total demand deposits. This was necessary due to the nature in which the goals were formulated (i.e., diversification as a percentage of total deposits). The number of variables is somewhat irrelevant. Any number of variables could conceivably have been used. It is basically dependent on what the bank wants from its diversification. Reserves and cash are mandatory for a bank; therefore, it was necessary to have a single variable for these assets. This model assumes that a certain percentage of total deposits are to be in total loans, hence, a single variable could have been used. Four variables were used, however, because they show more clearly the composition of loans. Goals could then be further constructed to account for these subsets if desired (i.e., commercial loans as 40% of total loans).

The same logic would also be true for deposits. Since diversification is based on total deposits, a single variable could again have been used. Three variables were used because they show the composition of deposits and, if desired, allow

Exhibit 8.1 LGP Model for Texas National Savings Bank

Variables:

x_1 = Reserves and cash

x_2 = Demand deposits

x_3 = Interest bearing checking accounts

x_4 = Savings and time deposits

x_5 = Commercial loans

x_6 = Installment loans

x_7 = Correspondent loans

x_8 = Real estate loans

x_9 = Treasury bills

x_{10} = Long-term governments

x_{11} = Muncipal bonds and others

Objective Function:

Minimize: $Z = P_0(d_1^- + d_1^+) + P_1(d_2^- + d_2^+) + P_2(d_3^- + d_3^+) + P_3(d_4^- + d_4^+) + P_4(d_5^-) + P_5(d_6^+)$

Constraints:

$$x_1 + x_5 + x_6 + x_7 + x_8 + x_9 + x_{10} + x_{11} - x_2 - x_3 - x_4 + d_1^- - d_1^+ = 0$$
(Linear equality constraint)

$$x_1 + d_2^- - d_2^+ = .15$$
(Reserve and cash constraint)

$$.4x_5 + .25x_6 + .15x_7 + .2x_8 + d_3^- - d_3^+ = .65$$
(Loan constraints)

$$.6x_9 + .25x_{10} + .15x_{11} + d_4^- - d_4^+ = .20$$
(Investment security constraint)

$$.13x_5 + .13x_6 + .12x_7 + .15x_8 + .09x_9 + .11x_{10} + .08x_{11} + d_5^- - d_5^+ = .12$$
(Rate of return constraint)

$$.24x_5 + .29x_6 + .19x_7 + .19x_8 + .1x_{11} + d_6^- - d_6^+ = .14$$
(Risk constraint)

$$x_j, d_i^-, d_i^+ \geq 0$$

further goals to be constructed. For these reasons three variables were used for investment securities as well.

A further reason that multiple variables were used for total loans, total deposits, and the investment securities categories is that the risk and return ratings would have been difficult to apply to a combined category. For example, real estate loans are generally not as risky of default as installment loans. Real estate loans are highly secured loans, and it would be misleading to assign the same risk rating to them as to an installment loan. The same type of logic holds true for returns as well. Not all accounts generate the same amount in return; therefore, to assign the same coefficient of return to all classes of investment assets would be illogical and incorrect.

The five prioritized goals of this model are simplistic in nature, but they represent the major objectives or requirements of TNSB concerning the diversification of its deposits with regard to safety and profitability. Reserve requirements are not only a goal of a bank, they are a requirement by law as well. Cash due from banks is combined with these reserves to provide a necessary level of bank safety and solvency. Profitability enters in the second and third goals. These are the loan and investment security diversification goal objectives of TNSB. The percentage coefficients were subjectively adapted using TNSB balance sheet numbers from the last year which in turn were averaged and rounded for convenience. Although they may not be representative of all banks, they attempt to show how TNSB can at least adapt or construct its objectives into goals to fit this model. The rate of return goal value was strictly an assumption made regarding the return on the investment assets due to the diversification of deposits. The effective return percentages are presented in Exhibit 8.2. The risk coefficient goal is also subjectively derived. The risk coefficients are also presented in Exhibit 8.2. The coefficients of risk relate to default risk and were subjectively derived by talking to bank officers and by assumptions regarding the risks factors in relation to the different loan and investment security assets used in this model. In order to make these percentages, the coefficient

Exhibit 8.2 Effective Return and Risk Coefficient

Variable	Investment Asset	Effective Return	Risk Coefficient*	Relative Risk Coefficient**
x_1	Cash	0	0	0
x_5	Commercial loans	13	5	.24
x_6	Installment loans	13	6	.29
x_7	Correspndent loans	12	4	.19
x_8	Real estate loans	15	4	.19
x_9	Treasury bills	9	0	0
x_{10}	Long-term governments	11	0	0
x_{11}	Municipal bonds and others	8	2	.1

*The higher the number, the greater the possibility of default.
**These values were found by summing the Risk Coefficient column (i.e., $5+6+4+4+2 = 22$) and dividing this amount back into each of the values in that column. The right-hand-side value represents the goal of $3/21 = .14$ used in the Risk Constraint.

number from Exhibit 8.2 was divided by the sum of the risk coefficients. These percentages are then used in the model in a manner consistent with the previous constraints. The return coefficients are also somewhat subjective. They are assumed to be net costs or effective (gross) rates of interest on the various investment assets. These gross rates of interest were derived in part from the *Federal Reserve Bulletin* and adapted for use in this model. It was necessary to use these rates because some funds are more expensive to service than others. Two simplifying assumptions are apparent here. The cost of funds are assumed to be the same for all investment assets. Also, there is no maturity matching within this model.

Before discussing the solution generated by this LGP model, President Sanco asked for suggestions on how to implement the model and its future usage. This model shows that a bank's assets can be divided into certain components. Cash and reserves, loans, and investment securities are all considered in the model. Management's policies and decisions can identify and measure the importance of the interrelationships which exist between these two components. In effect, then, the decisions regarding loan and investment strategies are tied to the decisions of management. This model can be used to derive the best solution regarding the diversification of deposits into the various investment assets of a bank. An asset-management model of this type can be used to allow management to make better decisions based on the quantitative information available and the goals they wish to achieve.

This type of model could also be used in a strict investment portfolio selection scenario, for the scheduling of workers, or in some type of credit scoring model. Marketing and liquidity management are also important areas where various forms of this type of LGP model are being used as well as financial planning, computer timing, and profitability accounting.

CHAPTER QUESTIONS

8.1 Did Johnson Smith complete his assignment? What did he fail to do, if anything?

8.2 Determine the solution for the problem stated in Exhibit 8.1. Explain the solution in detail as though you were presenting the results to bank officers.

8.3 Why did Johnson Smith place the deviational variable for the first goal constraint at P_0?

SELECTED REFERENCES

Keown, A.J., "A Chance-Constrained Goal Programming Model for Bank Liquidity Management," *Decision Sciences,* Vol. , No. 1, (January, 1981), pp. 93–106.

Sealy, C.W., Jr., "Commercial Bank Portfolio Management with Multiple Objectives," *Journal of Commercial Bank Lending,* Vol. 59, No. 6, (February, 1977), pp. 39–48.

Wilsted, W.D.; Hendrick, T.E.; and Steward, T.R., "Judgment Policy Capturing for Bank Loan Decisions: An Approach to Developing Objective Functions for Goal Programming Models," *Journal of Management Studies,* Vol. 12, No. 2, (May, 1975), pp. 210–225.

9

Xanaire National Telecommunication System

Xanaire is a small country located in northeast Africa. Having obtained its independence from France in the early 1960's, Xanaire started building the Xanaire National Telecommunication System (XNTS). In 1980, the XNTS consisted of six telecommunication centers, located at militaristically strategic points throughout Xanaire. The telecommunication centers were each equipped with the same number of government personnel and the same type of telecommunication facilities. To distribute the message taking and receiving activities required, each center was assigned a customer service territory. These territories are presented in Exhibit 9.1. Each customer service territory contained at least one military base and one major city. Customers, both government and public, who wished to send a message, were required to do so at the telecommunication center they were assigned to, by territory.

In October of 1980, Samual Como, the Director of XNTS, invited Sandy Cho, a personnel consultant from an American corporation located in Xanaire, to assist him in his 1981 personnel planning session. (Sandy Cho's services were being offered to the Xanaire government as a community service by the American corporation she worked for.) Upon meeting the Director of XNTS, who also is a Colonel in the Xanaire National Army, Sandy and the Director discussed the personnel allocation problem at the telecommunication centers under the Director's jurisdiction.

SAMUAL COMO: Each year in October we must plan our next year's personnel needs at each of the six telecommunication centers across Xanaire. Since the staffing requirements at one center are basically the same for the other centers, we use a single center to model our personnel allocation decisions for all the centers. What

Exhibit 9.1   Telecommunication Service Territories within Xanaire

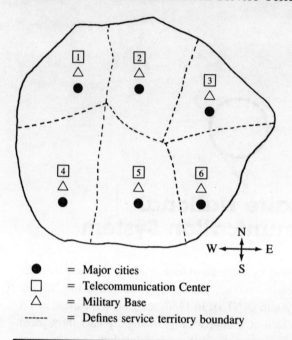

●	= Major cities
▢	= Telecommunication Center
△	= Military Base
------	= Defines service territory boundary

we would like to do this year is develop a personnel planning model that will help us optimally allocate our telecommunication personnel. As I am sure you know, Ms. Cho, a telecommunication center's function is to transmit and receive message traffic for its assigned customer territory. The telecommunication centers recently had a mission change which authorized a possible increase in manning in the telecommunication center from 14 to 19 operators (i.e., the people who transmit and receive messages). To fill these new authorizations, five additional operators can be recruited. Currently, each center now operates with seven qualified personnel, seven trainees and, if need be, the possible addition of five more operators. This situation heavily taxes the qualified operators to train newcomers, maintain message traffic, and minimize error rates. Optimal use of the qualified operators to educate trainees and manning equipment is necessary. Until a trainee fulfills all required tasks is certified and completes the minimum 12 months' training time, a trainer must review all work and directly supervise each assigned trainee.

The telecommunication centers are the primary means for transmitting government originated classified messages. They also have a heavy load of general public unclassified messages that, due to time constraints, must be transmitted. Our research indicates that, on average, a qualified operator can transmit a message in approximately 15 minutes. Any errors in classification, addressing or parity will be caught at the automatic switching center and will result in errors documented against the certifying operator. A message electrically received at the center for delivery to a customer is processed, on average, in approximately six minutes.

Due to the critical nature of the work performed in the center, fatigue and morale are also important. The efficient allocation of operators to process message traffic expeditiously with a minimum of errors, while training inexperienced personnel, is a constant problem of the communications operations officer. Assigning operators to shifts which will optimize his/her objectives and maintain high morale is the problem we face each year in our personnel planning sessions. The 14 current operators are required to transmit and receive electrical messages, maintain facility cleanliness, and perform other duties as directed. Workdays are divided into three shifts: 0800–1600, 1600–2400, and 2400–0800. In reality, the operators must report 20 minutes earlier to perform inventories and be ready to assume their duties at the start of the shift. Due to the nature of their work and stress involved, each operator should not work more than 40 hours per week, although 60-hour weeks are not uncommon. Excess fatigue has shown to increase error rates and security violations. Using data to predict message traffic patterns, error rates, and training needs, the assignments must be based on: shift, type operator, message traffic, error rate, training, and facility maintenance. What we need is a model that will solve for the optimal shift placement of qualified and unqualified operators (i.e., trainees) given the realistic constraints observed in the problem situation. As a government consultant, Ms. Cho, you have been given complete military clearance and may obtain any data or information necessary to develop your model. As the Director of XNTS, I would like you to incorporate in your model the following objectives:

1.   Since we currently have 14 personnel at each center, and message traffic has continually increased, please make sure you fully utilize all of the current staff.

2.   Since the centers transmit classified messages, provide some measure of security and/or safety in the accuracy of the messages.

3.   Do your best to provide sufficient personnel to cover maximum daily message traffic demands.

4.   Provide a sufficient number of qualified personnel to help train the newly hired center trainees.

5.   Provide sufficient personnel to minimize message error rates.

6.   While five additional personnel have been authorized for each center, try to minimize their use.

7.   Provide sufficient extra personnel to allow for adequate maintenance to the telecommunication facilities.

Obviously, not all of these objectives can be fully achieved, but do what you can to satisfy as many as you can. The Xanaire government would also like you to present your model and personnel allocation solution at our December meeting this year. We will be particularly interested in how you formulate the model and all necessary assumptions. Good luck, and if I can help you obtain any information please feel free to call on me.

SANDY CHO: It looks like a challenge. I'll do my best.

In December of 1980, Sandy Cho returned to the office of the Director of XNTS and presented the results of her research.

SANDY CHO: The following are the definitions and explanations of the variables, constants, prioritized goals, goal constraints and the objective function of the model:

■ Variables
General:

X_{ij}	=	The number of operators, dependent on the individual skill level and number of trainees i assigned to shift j where i = 1, 2, 3, 4; j = 1, 2, 3. These variables must be $\geq$ zero and integer
d_k^-, d_k^+	=	Deviation variables from k different goals
Z	=	The sum of all deviational variables

Specific:
Manpower

x_{1j}	=	Trainees
x_{2j}	=	Fully qualified operator with no assigned trainees
x_{3j}	=	Fully qualified operator with 1 assigned trainee
x_{4j}	=	Fully qualified operator with 2 assigned trainees

Shift

x_{i1}	=	0800–1600 shift
x_{i2}	=	1600–2400 shift
x_{i3}	=	2400–0800 shift

■ Constraints

t_i	=	Maximum number of message transmissions processed per ith type operator for an eight hour shift
r_i	=	Maximum number of message receptions processed for ith type operator for an eight hour shift

156

T_j = Total number of message transmissions required to be processed per each jth shift of operators

R_j = Total number of message receptions required to be processed per each jth shift of operators

e_{ij} = Percentage message error rate for the ith operator in the jth shift

■ Priority Goals

P_1 = Fully utilize available manpower

P_2 = Insure message security/safety

P_3 = Satisfy maximum message traffic demand

P_4 = Train new personnel

P_5 = Minimize message error rate

P_6 = Minimize additional use of manpower

P_7 = Provide adequate maintenance of facilities

■ Goal Constraints

(P_1) Manpower Constraints

A total of 14 operators are assigned to the telecommunications centers. Since the government does not pay overtime and the mission must be accomplished, the total number of operators may be utilized. To minimize fatigue and maintain a satisfactory level of morale, work schedules should be limited to 40 hours per week. Of the 14 operators, seven are fully qualified. Underutilization will result in operators being used in other operations within the center.

$$\sum_{i=1}^{4} \sum_{j=1}^{3} x_{ij} + d_1^{-M} - d_1^{+M} = 14$$

$$\sum_{i=2}^{4} \sum_{j=1}^{3} x_{ij} + d_2^{-M} - d_2^{+M} = 7$$

(P_2) Security/Safety Constraints

To insure safety and provide dual check security, at least two operators should be assigned per shift. Violations of security can result in disciplinary actions varying from administrative action to general court-martial.

$$\sum_{i=2}^{4} x_{ij} + d_k^{-SS} - d_k^{+SS} = 2 \quad \text{(for } j = 1, 2, 3; k = 3, 4, 5)$$

(P_3) Message Traffic Constraints

The highest traffic totals predicted for a routine shift are used. Emergency situations would necessitate recall of any off-duty personnel, but this is not taken into

157

account. Based on historical records of the operating personnel, the message transmission and reception times were estimated.

The number of maximum transmissions, t_{ij}, processed per operator for an eight hour shift are found to be $t_{1j} = 16$, $t_{2j} = 32$, $t_{3j} = 8$ and $t_{4j} = 0$ for each of the $j = 1, 2, 3$ shifts. The number of maximum receptions, r_{ij}, processed per operator for an eight hour shift was found to be $r_{1j} = 32$, $r_{2j} = 80$, $r_{3j} = 32$ and $r_{4j} = 0$ for each of the $j = 1, 2, 3$ shifts. Using the time a qualified operator can perform a transmission (15 minutes) and reception (6 minutes), a ratio was set up to determine the average amount of time spent per shift on each function. (Transmission ratio $-$ (15 min/TX) (60 TX) $\div$ [(15 min/TX) (60 TX) + (6 min/RF) (180 RX) = .45].) Checking all shifts would show that each spent approximately 45 percent of their time doing transmissions and 55 percent doing receptions. For a busy day the traffic totals for transmit and receive were estimated per shift to be: transmissions per shift, (T_j), $T_1 = 60$, $T_2 = 75$ and $T_3 = 15$; receptions per shift, (R_j), $R_1 = 180$, $R_2 = 225$, and $R_3 = 45$. Based on the information above, goal restraints will require the solution to reflect the number and type of operators assigned to each shift to handle non-emergency traffic.

$$\sum_{i=1}^{4} .45 x_{ij} \, t_{ij} + d_k^{-MT} - d_k^{+MT} = T_j \quad (\text{for } j = 1, 2, 3; \, k = 6, 7, 8)$$

$$\sum_{i=1}^{4} .55 x_{ij} \, r_{ij} + d_k^{-MT} - d_k^{+MT} = R_j \quad (\text{for } j = 1, 2, 3; \, k = 9, 10, 11)$$

(P₄) Training Constraints

To enhance training, one trainer per trainee is best; however, a limit of two trainees per trainer should not be exceeded. Assigning more does not violate training regulations, but through personal experience and interviews with telecommunication center supervisors, this is a maximum number for an acceptable level of training. To achieve this goal, two types of constraints are needed—to assign one trainee to a fully qualified operator and a second to assign two trainees to a fully qualified operator.

$$x_{3j} - x_{1j} - d_k^{+T} = 0 \quad (\text{for } j = 1, 2, 3; \, k = 12, 13, 14)$$
$$x_{4j} - .5 x_{1j} - d_k^{+T} = 0 \quad (\text{for } j = 2, 3, 4; \, k = 15, 16, 17)$$

(P₅) Error Rate Constraint

Error rate is a primary measure of the center's transmission effectiveness. Since the error rate is accountable to only qualified operator trainees, x_{1j} will not be considered. The current governmental standard was found to be .01. Obviously a negative deviation is desirable, thus a positive deviation may indicate that remedial training is necessary. The average error rates were found to be .008 for a x_{2j}, .009 for a x_{3j} and .016 for a x_{4j}. The x_{1j} is not considered for error rate because his/her trainer is credited with the errors and also with their transmissions. The error rate for a center is found by adding the product of the error rate per trained operator times the ratio of the transmission accredited that operator per shift divided by the total transmission for all operators per shift. The sum of the individual trained operator's percentage of error can then be compared with the current government standard of .01 in a goal constraint.

$$\sum_{i=2}^{4}\sum_{j=1}^{3}e_{ij}\frac{\left(\sum_{l=1}^{4}\sum_{m=1}^{3}t_{ij}\right)}{T_j}\;x_{ij}\;+\;d_{18}^{-E}\;-\;d_{18}^{+E}\;=\;.01$$

$$\text{(for select } l = 1, 2, 3, 4; \; m = 1, 2, 3)$$

(P₆) Additional Manpower Use Constraint

Although a total of 14 operators are available, it is possible to exceed that number by additional manning assistance. This assistance would be very costly on government funds and should be minimized. Research on available manning resources at the telecommunications center revealed a maximum (i.e., realistically cost effective) of five additional operators could be added to the present total number of operators.

$$\sum_{i=1}^{4}\sum_{j=1}^{3}x_{ij}\;+\;d_{19}^{-AM}\;-\;d_{19}^{+AM}\;=\;19$$

(P₇) Facilitates Maintenance Constraint

Every center is assigned facilities maintenance responsibilities. Message traffic is the operators' primary function; however, clean-up (washing, waxing, painting, etc.) is a secondary and very visible responsibility. Facility maintenance must be functionally related to the manpower variables of the model. So, a fixed manpower allocation had to be assessed to represent adequate coverage of manpower effort for total facilities maintenance. Observations on personnel revealed that the equivalent of one operator could cover all three shifts if his/her eight hour time period were spread over the 24-hour day. This is the same as .33 of an operator being allocated for facilities maintenance per shift. By adding one additional person to the current staff of 14 and minimizing the negative deviation from the 15, we will add the necessary additional staff for facility maintenance purposes.

$$\sum_{i=1}^{4}\sum_{j=1}^{3}x_{ij}\;+\;d_{20}^{-FM}\;-\;d_{20}^{+FM}\;=\;15$$

■ Objective Function

The objective function seeks to minimize the value of each of the deviational variables included within it. At P_1, we seek to minimize both positive and negative deviation from the stated right-hand-side values of available personnel. Thus, both the positive and negative deviational variables will be included in the objective function at P_1. P_2 is our goal of message security. Safety will be achieved if at least two operators are assigned per shift. We can have more than two, but it is desirable not to have less. So we will only include the negative deviational variables in the objective function. For P_3, our goals were set at the maximum levels of message reception and transmissions. Our goal is to have adequate personnel to cover the message load, and so we include only the negative deviational variables in the objective function. At P_4, our goal is to provide adequate training coverage. This limits the number of trainees to be assigned to two or less fully qualified operators. We can model this by including only the positive deviational variables in the objective function. For P_5, we seek to assign operators by shifts to minimize message error rates. Our goal is to minimize positive deviation from the Xanaire Government standard. To accomplish the modeling of this desire, we would include only the positive deviational variables in the objective function. At P_6, our goal is to minimize additional manpower usage. We can accomplish this by including only the positive deviational variable in the objective function. Finally, at P_7, we seek to provide adequate facilities maintenance. We can model this desire by including only the negative deviational variable in the objective function.

The resulting objective function can be expressed as follows:

$$\text{Minimize:} \quad Z = P_1(d_{1,2}^{-M} + d_{1,2}^{+M}) + P_2(\sum_{k=3}^{5} d_k^{-SS}) + P_3(\sum_{k=6}^{11} d_k^{-MT})$$

$$+ P_4(\sum_{k=12}^{17} d^{+T}) + P_5(d_{18}^{+E}) + P_6(d_{19}^{+AM}) + P_7(d_{20}^{-FM})$$

■ Solution

The formulation for the Xanaire Telecommunication Center's personnel allocation problem required seven priorities, 20 goal constraints, 12 personnel variables and 38 deviational variables. A Fortran program, capable of solving a goal programming integer problem, was used on an IBM 370/168 computer system. The required CPU time to solve this problem was less than nine seconds. The solution results are presented in Exhibit 9.2. The solution to the personnel allocation problem for the Xanaire Telecommunication Center satisfied four of the seven goals (i.e., P_1, P_2, P_4, and P_6). Unfortunately, several goals (P_3, P_5, and P_7) were not fully satisfied. The question now is whether the solution, while optimal in a mathematical sense, is feasible from an implementation standpoint.

■ Implementation and Limitations

Making adjustments to the model to arrive at an implementable alternative solution as well as the model's limitations are of importance in the use of the LGP model.

If the fact that P_3, P_5, and P_7 were not achieved or the amount by which they were not achieved is unacceptable for a solution, goal programming permits us

Exhibit 9.2 Goal Programming Solution for a Xanaire Telecommunication Center*

Personnel Assignments

Variable = Allocation	Explanation
$x_{11} = 1, x_{31} = 1$	Two operators will be assigned to the 1st shift; a trainee and his/her instructor for a 12-month period.
$x_{12} = 5, x_{32} = 5$	Ten operators will be assigned to the 2nd shift; five trainees and their five respective instructors for a 12-month time period.
$x_{13} = 1, x_{33} = 1$	Two operators will be assigned to the 3rd shift; a trainee and his/her instructor for a 12-month time period.

Goal Accomplishment

Priority = Goal Deviation	Explanation
$P_1 = 0$	This goal is fully satisfied. All 14 operators will be allocated to satisfy the demand for their services. Also, only seven operators will be required to be fully qualified.
$P_2 = 0$	This goal is fully satisfied. At least two operators will be allocated to each shift.
$P_3 = 8030$ (negative)	This goal is not fully satisfied. A total of 744 transmissions and 7,286 receptions under the required maximum levels will not be achieved.
$P_4 = 0$	This goal is fully satisfied. No more than one trainee was assigned to a fully qualified operator.
$P_5 = .004$ (positive)	This goal is not fully satisfied. An expected error of .014 (or .004 over the Division standard) will be achieved.
$P_6 = 0$	This goal is fully satisfied. No additional manning personnel will be required.
$P_7 = 1$ (negative)	This goal is not fully satisfied. The additional operator for facility maintenance will not be allocated.

*All other x_{ij} variables not listed in table are zero.

some flexibility in altering the solution. First, we could change the priority structure by shifting goals to different priority levels. For example, we could shift the goal of meeting message traffic demands (i.e., P_3) to P_1 and move the goal of fully utilizing available manpower (P_1) to P_3. Then we would rerun the model and see the effect of the shifted goals on the resulting solution. This type of sensitivity analysis can be repeated for all combinations of the priority levels that judgmental opinions would reason feasible. The model may result in an alternative solution that is both feasible and acceptable.

A second alternative solution can be brought about by changing one or more parameters in the existing model. Which parameter to change is best determined by using common sense. For example, in the telecommunication center problem, we can logically reason that the addition of, say, one more fully qualified operator should reduce the number of transmissions/receptions (P_3) and facility maintenance that would not be done (P_7) if the existing solution is implemented. If the additional operator is fully qualified, he/she might also help, on the average, to reduce the total error rate (P_5). This alternative solution can be brought about by changing the right-hand-side values of the first goal constraints from 14 to 15 and second goal constraint from 7 to 8. Having changed the parameter, the model would then be rerun and the new solution evaluated.

Whatever approach is selected to change the resulting solution, it should be obvious that little effort is needed by the person using the model to make the change. The results of the change, though, might have a dramatic improvement in the solution. Also, it should be obvious that it takes much less time to change a parameter and revise the model to determine an alternative solution, than mentally rethinking a revised alternative solution.

One major limitation on the use of the proposed model is its use of estimated goal constraint parameters. Since any model's output (or solution) is only as good as the model's input, estimation of such model parameters as maximum and total message transmissions/receptions and message error rates are critical in the accuracy of the model's solution. In addition to using judgmental opinion, a more accurate approach would be to use a time study method to develop precise measures of work performance on the specific operations. The two-month time period given for this study did not permit the use of such time-consuming data collection methods.

CHAPTER QUESTIONS

9.1 How would you evaluate Sandy Cho's consulting work? Did she do what she was asked to do?

9.2 What modeling assumptions does Sandy's LGP model require for its results to be valid?

9.3 Do you feel the LGP model and its solution are acceptable or do you feel the model should be revised? If you feel it should be revised, what, if any, additional information do you need?

SELECTED REFERENCES

Bres, E.S.; Burns, D.; Charnes, A.; and Cooper, W.W. "A Goal Programming Model for Planning Officer Accessions," *Management Science,* Vol. 26, No. 6, (August, 1980), pp. 773–783.

Lee, S.M.; Franz, L.S.; and Wynne, A.J., "Optimizing State Patrol Manpower Allocations," *Journal of the Operational Research Society,* Vol. 30, No. 10, (October, 1979), pp. 885–896.

Price, W.L., "A Review of Mathematical Models in Human Resource Planning," *OMEGA,* Vol. 8, No. 6, (1980), pp. 639–645.

Houghton
School
System

The Houghton School System (HSS) is located in Missouri. HSS is a public school system consisting of six elementary schools (grades K to 6), three junior-high schools (grades 7 to 9) and two high schools (i.e., grades 10 to 12). These schools are spread over a rural area of 3,000 square miles. In 1980, HSS provided education to over 20,000 students.

In June of 1980, HSS received a grant from the federal government under Title I of the Elementary and Secondary Education School Act to hire six new educational support personnel. The support personnel were hired to provide educational support to the existing elementary grade school teachers in the form of teacher workshops (i.e., to educate the teachers) and inclass assistance (i.e., to educate the students) in the specialized areas of mathematics and reading.

In complying with both state and federal regulations, each of the six support personnel were required to teach morning classes at one school and then teach the afternoon classes at a second school. Each of the six grade schools would also have to receive educational support in both mathematics and reading each day of the week. This required support personnel to travel between two schools each day. Unfortunately, this also necessitated traveling expenses for the educational support personnel. At the same time, the federal government expected the HSS to utilize the grant money as efficiently as possible. Sufficient funds were available to pay for travel expenses, supplies, and program planning development.

The HSS Superintendant, Lance Jones, decided to hire a consultant to develop an assignment schedule for the educational support personnel. Betty Smith, owner of Smith Consulting Service, was offered the scheduling job by Mr. Jones in July of 1980.

Betty began by gathering data on the traveling distance among the six grade schools the educational support personnel would travel. This information is presented in Exhibit 10.1. HSS had agreed to reimburse the six support personnel at a rate of $.18 per mile for the trip between the grade schools that each of the support personnel would be required to make each day. HSS would like to minimize this transportation reimbursement expense.

Exhibit 10.1   Distance in Miles Between the Grade Schools

Schools	Schools					
	1	2	3	4	5	6
1	0	34	43	47	65	65
2	34	0	30	27	32	40
3	43	30	0	61	40	63
4	47	27	61	0	50	20
5	65	32	40	50	0	25
6	65	40	63	20	25	0

Betty also found that the school system superintendent had several additional goals to accomplish besides cost minimization. One of these additional goals involved improving the use of micro computers in two of the grade schools. One of the newly hired educational support personnel had an extensive micro computer education. She could provide much-needed micro computer instruction to the grade school staff of the two schools (i.e., grades 4 and 5) that had just received new micro computer equipment, if she were assigned to those two schools. Another goal of the superintendant is to minimize potential personality problems. The superintendent noticed at recent staff meetings that some of the newly hired support personnel have personalities that clashed with some of the grade school principals. To avoid these personality clashes, it is desirable to not assign the same person to teach in the morning at Grade School 2 and then to teach in the afternoon at Grade School 4. Also, no support personnel should be assigned to teach in the morning at Grade School 4 and then teach in the afternoon at Grade School 6.

After considering the data collected and the superintendent's scheduling desires, Betty decided to formulate the assignment problem as an LGP problem. The model she developed is presented in Exhibit 10.2.

One of the conditions Betty had to agree to in accepting this consulting job concerned the HSS payment for her consulting services. Mr. Jones offered her 70

Exhibiti 10.2 LGP Formulation of the Houghton School System Assignment Problem

Minimize: $Z = P_1(d_1^- + \ldots + d_{11}^- + d_1^+ + \ldots + d_{11}^+) + P_2(d_{12}^- + d_{12}^+)$
$+ P_3(d_{13}^+ + d_{14}^+) + P_4 d_{15}^+$

subject to:

$$x_{12} + x_{13} + x_{14} + x_{15} + x_{16} + d_1^- - d_1^+ = 1$$
$$x_{21} + x_{23} + x_{24} + x_{25} + x_{26} + d_2^- - d_2^+ = 1$$
$$x_{31} + x_{32} + x_{34} + x_{35} + x_{36} + d_3^- - d_3^+ = 1$$
$$x_{41} + x_{42} + x_{43} + x_{45} + x_{46} + d_4^- - d_4^+ = 1$$
$$x_{51} + x_{52} + x_{53} + x_{54} + x_{56} + d_5^- - d_5^+ = 1$$
$$x_{61} + x_{62} + x_{63} + x_{64} + x_{65} + d_6^- - d_6^+ = 1$$
$$x_{12} + x_{21} + x_{31} + x_{41} + x_{51} + x_{61} + d_7^- - d_7^+ = 1$$
$$x_{13} + x_{23} + x_{32} + x_{42} + x_{52} + x_{62} + d_8^- - d_8^+ = 1$$
$$x_{14} + x_{24} + x_{34} + x_{43} + x_{53} + x_{63} + d_9^- - d_9^+ = 1$$
$$x_{15} + x_{25} + x_{35} + x_{45} + x_{54} + x_{64} + d_{10}^- - d_{10}^+ = 1$$
$$x_{16} + x_{26} + x_{36} + x_{46} + x_{56} + x_{65} + d_{11}^- - d_{11}^+ = 1$$
$$x_{45} + d_{12}^- - d_{12}^+ = 1$$
$$x_{24} \qquad - d_{13}^+ = 0$$
$$x_{46} \qquad - d_{14}^+ = 0$$

$$34x_{12} + 43x_{13} + 47x_{14} + 65x_{15} + 65x_{16}$$
$$+ 34x_{21} + 30x_{23} + 27x_{24} + 32x_{25} + 40x_{26}$$
$$+ 43x_{31} + 30x_{32} + 61x_{34} + 40x_{35} + 63x_{36}$$
$$+ 47x_{41} + 27x_{42} + 61x_{43} + 50x_{45} + 20x_{46}$$
$$+ 65x_{51} + 32x_{52} + 40x_{53} + 50x_{54} + 25x_{56}$$
$$+ 65x_{61} + 40x_{62} + 63x_{63} + 20x_{64} + 25x_{65} - d_{15}^+ = 0$$

and $\quad x_{ij} = 0$ or 1
$\quad d_i^-, d_i^+ \geq 0$

where:

x_{ij} = the assignment of support personnel among the $n \times n - n$ possible assignments. The ith subscript represents the school the support personnel would work at in the morning, and the jth subscript represents the afternoon assignment.

d_i^- = the assignment of less than one person to the grade school (where $i = 1, \ldots, 12$)

d_i^+ = the assignment of more than one person to the grade school (where $i = 1, \ldots, 12$)

d_{13}^+ = the assignment of someone to travel between grade schools 2 and 4

d_{14}^+ = the assignment of someone to travel between grade schools 4 and 6

d_{15}^+ = total daily miles traveled between grade schools for all educational support personnel

P_1 = priority level representing the goal of allocating the six educational support personnel to the six grade schools

167

P_2 = priority level representing the goal of assigning a support personnel to grade school 4 and 5

P_3 = priority level representing the goal of not assigning support personnel between grade schools 2 and 4 and also between grade schools 4 and 6

P_4 = priority level representing the goal of minimizing traveling distance for all six support personnel

---

percent of the cost savings incurred by using her assignment schedule. Mr. Jones conservatively estimated that each of the six support personnel would on average travel 60 miles a day for 180 school days. At $.18 per mile, that would result in $11,664 reimbursable travel expenses. The $11,664 is budgeted for the 1980–81 school year for traveling expenses. Any reduction from the 1980–81 school year budget figure represents a cost savings.

CHAPTER QUESTIONS

10.1 What is the optimal assignment schedule? Do the decision variables in the model in Exhibit 10.2 adequately serve to assign the support personnel? Write a precise assignment schedule defining who will be at which school, teaching reading or mathematics subjects and at what time of day.

10.2 Based on the optimal assignment schedule, what is Betty going to be paid for her consulting services?

10.3 Can a better solution be developed that will satisfy more of the goals stated in the problem? Use sensitivity analysis to determine all other possible goal combinations and their respective solutions.

SELECTED REFERENCES

Lee, S.M., and Schniederjans, M.J., "A Multi-Criteria Assignment Problem: A Goal Programming Approach," *Interfaces,* Vol. 13, No. 4, (August, 1983), pp. 75–81.

Mehta, A.J., and Rifai, A.K., "Application of Linear Programming vs. Goal Programming to Assignment Problem," *Akron Business and Economic Review,* Vol. 7, No. 4, (Winter, 1976), pp. 52–55.

Saladin, A., "Goal Programming Applied to Police Patrol Allocation," *Journal of Operations Management,* Vol. 2, No. 4, (August, 1982), pp. 239–249.

11
Lion
Construction
Corporation

In March of 1980, the Lion Construction Corporation (LCC), a satellite corporation of United States Construction Corporation, received a construction project ideally suited for their operation. The president of LCC, Ollie Schneider, III, engaged two consultants to advise him on planning the project. The consultants, Rosalie Jans and Lisa DiNoto, are recent MBA's and did not possess a great deal of experience in project planning in the construction industry. Fortunately, President Schneider was aware of the consultants' lack of industry experience and prepared a rather complete orientation for the consultants.

PRESIDENT SCHNEIDER: Major construction corporations have split themselves into small corporations in the past few decades. The home office, or parent corporation, usually owns all construction equipment associated with the related corporations. The parent corporation leases the equipment to the satellite corporations for construction purposes. Satellite corporations can be organized by geographic region, such as a Western Group or Southern Group, or they can be organized by function, such as Mining Group or Building Group. The purpose of this leasing procedure is to protect the conglomerate from bankruptcies. For instance, if a satellite corporation failed miserably on a project and lost millions of dollars, the parent company would still retain the equipment. The satellite corporation keep capital assets at a minimum so if they go bankrupt they do not lose as much. The leased assets revert back to the parent company. This legal maneuvering reduces the chances for losing capital equipment, but it creates a transfer pricing headache. The LCC is a satellite corporation of the United States Construction Corporation

169

Exhibit 11.1   Aerial View of Osage River, Earth Disposal Sites and Settling Ponds*

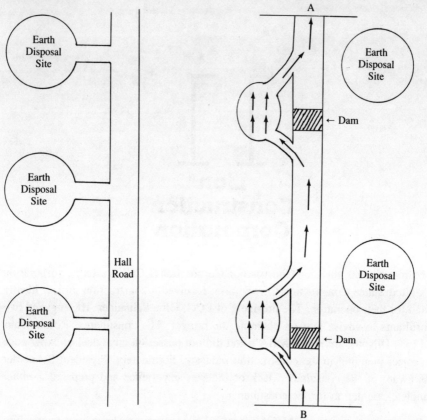

*The boundary between Line A and Line B defines the section of the Osage River to be excavated.

owned by my father. LCC primarily handles the earth-moving aspects of a construction project. Other satellite corporations handle the rest of the project.

One of the most difficult tasks facing our corporation and in particular our construction manager is in choosing the right heavy equipment for the job at hand. Construction managers usually rely on their personal experiences and intuition when they pick the heavy equipment that will be used on a particular job. Generally, construction managers do not apply formal systematic analyses to the allocation problem. Currently, the construction manager receives computer printouts from the parent corporation that display typical production rates for different equipment pieces over different haul distances. The construction manager would also obtain cost data for the various equipment pieces (i.e., operating costs, ownership costs, and repair costs). Based on the characteristics of the project, the construction manager identifies the equipment that is applicable for the task.

What LCC would like you consultants to do for us is develop a model to optimize the selection of construction equipment that is dependent on the amount of material to be moved and the distance it must be hauled before dumping. We would like to build an initial decision model based on a particular earth-moving project LCC is currently facing. We would then like you to explain to us how we can alter the model so it can be used for decision-making in other similar earth-moving projects.

This particular project, the Kansas-Osage Waterway Project, involves the excavation of 16,000,000 cubic yards of earth in a 20-month period of time. The Osage River is to be transformed into a canal capable of handling river barges. An aerial view and cross-section view of the project site are presented in Exhibits 11.1 and 11.2 respectively. There is one major complicating factor on this job. The contract requires that a settling pond be installed at each end of the project. These settling ponds are used to remove silt from the river. The construction activity increases the amount of silt in the river, which is hazardous to fishlife. To counter this problem, the river is channeled in and out of settling ponds. When the river hits the slower moving body of water, the silt drops to the bottom. These ponds must be periodically dredged by a dragline. Besides the unusual settling ponds, this project will be accomplished using straightforward construction techniques. Therefore, historical production and cost data generated by the parent corporation will be applicable.

The available equipment and a brief description of their earth-moving function

Exhibit 11.2   Cross-Section View of Osage River and Proposed Finished Canal*

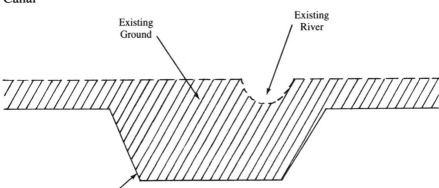

*The shaded portion of the existing ground represents the earth to be excavated.

for the Kansas-Osage Waterway Project is presented in Exhibit 11.3. The monthly earth-moving and hauling capabilities of each equipment piece is presented in Exhibit 11.4. The term "Production" refers here to the movement of earth. The information provided in Exhibit 11.4 was derived from historical records maintained by the parent company. In Exhibit 11.4, for example, a 21-cubic-yard scraper can move 7,000 cubic yards of earth over a haul distance of 0–500 feet, 29,300 cubic yards over a haul distance of 500–3,000 feet, and 8,900 cubic yards over a haul

---

Exhibit 11.3 Equipment Designations and Descriptions

Equipment Piece	Description
1. D8 Bulldozer	Generally used to push away stray piles of earth short distances.
2. D9 Bulldozer	Generally used to push away stray piles of earth short distances.
3. 21-Cubic-Yard Scraper (Self-Propelled)	Picks up earth by dropping a cutting edge approximately 8″ and "scraping" up the top few inches of soil.
4. 32-Cubic-Yard Scraper (Self-Propelled)	Picks up earth by dropping a cutting edge approximately 8″ and "scraping" up the top few inches of soil.
5. 11-Cubic-Yard Scraper (Elevating)	Picks up earth with a vertical conveyor belt. Cutting edges are attached to the conveyor. An elevating scraper loads its bin from the top while a self-propelled scraper loads its bin from the bottom.
6. 22-Cubic-Yard Scraper (Elevating)	Picks up earth with a vertical conveyor belt. Cutting edges are attached to the conveyor. An elevating scraper loads its bin from the top while a self-propelled scraper loads its bin from the bottom.
7. Two-Cubic-Yard Dragline	Crane-type piece of equipment. Casts a two-cubic-yard bucket with a line attached to it. The machine then "drags" the line back and the bucket comes with it. The bucket is maneuvered over a dumptruck and emptied.
8. Six-Cubic-Yard Truck	Used as part of the dragline operation. These trucks haul away the material excavated by the dragline.
9. 10-Cubic-Yard Truck	Used as part of the dragline operation. These trucks haul away the material excavated by the dragline.

Exhibit 11.4 Production Table for Various Pieces of Equipment—Cubic Yards Per Month

	Haul Distance (feet)		
Equipment	**0–500**	**500–3,000**	**3,000 +**
D8 Bulldozer	15,000	0	0
D9 Bulldozer	23,000	0	0
21-Cubic-Yard Scraper	7,000	29,300	8,900
32-Cubic-Yard Scraper	11,200	46,100	13,800
11-Cubic-Yard Scraper	2,300	9,100	2,600
22-Cubic-Yard Scraper	4,400	18,700	5,900
Two-Cubic-Yard Dragline	38,800	38,800	38,800
Six-Cubic-Yard Truck	0	4,300	10,800
10-Cubic-Yard Truck	0	7,200	18,000
TOTAL	200,000	900,000	300,000

Exhibit 11.5 Monthly Equipment Costs

Equipment Piece	**Monthly Cost ($)**
D8 Bulldozer	8,560
D9 Bulldozer	11,680
21-Cubic-Yard Scraper	12,060
32-Cubic-Yard Scraper	14,990
11-Cubic-Yard Scraper	6,870
22-Cubic-Yard Scraper	9,360
Two-Cubic-Yard Scraper	25,440
Six-Cubic-Yard Truck	15,990
10-Cubic-Yard Truck	21,320

distance of 3,000 + feet every month. The monthly equipment costs for each piece of equipment are presented in Exhibit 11.5.

The construction manager has the following typical construction goals in their order of importance:

1. Avoid the overutilization of draglines. Keep one dragline on the jobsite at all times.

2. Avoid making the dragline wait for a truck.

3. Attain the monthly average amount of earth that must be hauled 500–3,000 feet.

4. Attain the monthly average amount of earth that must be hauled 3,000+ feet.

5. Attain the monthly average amount of earth that must be hauled 0–500 feet.

6. Try to stay under budget.

7. Be prepared to go to a "push-pull" operation.

These goals can be explained in greater detail as follows:

1. *Dragline goal:* Generally, canal-type earth-moving projects require at least one dragline. There are certain tasks, such as clearing settling ponds, that only a dragline can do. While these jobs must be done only once every other month, they cannot be performed any earlier or later than every 30-day period. A dragline will spend one day emptying the sediment in a settlement pond then move toward the other pond during the rest of the month. This way, each pond is emptied every other month. Because a dragline is a rather cumbersome and awkward piece of equipment to transport, it is impractical to move it on and off the job site every month for one day of work. The dragline will perform its duties one day out of the month and then be utilized as best as possible during the remainder of the month. The construction manager must have at least one dragline on the job site so that the settlement ponds can be dredged as required. Due to the excessive cost of owning an idle dragline, the parent corporation controls only a limited number of draglines. The parent corporation will allocate more than one dragline to a project only if absolutely necessary.

2. *Dragline vs. production goal:* A dragline depends on trucks to haul away the earth it excavates. The optimal ratio of trucks to draglines varies according to bucket size on the dragline, load capacity of the trucks, and the haul distance the trucks must travel. A technique for determining the minimum number of trucks required to service a dragline requires one pick-up and one drop-off point. We suggest you use the longest haul distance possible to determine pick-up and drop-off locations. It is common knowledge in the construction industry that the major portion of the cost in truck hauling is in the loading process. The actual transporting and dumping of the material is a small part of the overall cost. Therefore, once a truck is loaded, it is desirable to assign it to the longest haul distance. Once haul distance is determined, the various ratios of dragline size to truck size can be determined from historical data. The formula we use is:

$$\sum_{i=0}^{n} \sum_{j=0}^{n} t_{ij} x_{ij}$$

where:

t = travel time,

$$x \;=\; \text{number of trucks,}$$
$$i \;=\; \text{starting point, and}$$
$$j \;=\; \text{destination}$$

Instead of a time or distance variable we use the equality of production rates, which are analogous. Traditionally, construction workers do not want their draglines standing idle, whether or not it made economic sense. The production of the trucks must therefore equal or exceed the production of the dragline.

3, 4, and 5. *Production goals:* The estimators and controllers in charge of this project have determined monthly production quotas that they would like the project manager to meet. During the bid preparation procedure it was determined that 4,000,000 cubic yards of earth must be hauled 0–500 feet, 18,000,000 cubic yards of earth must be hauled 500–3,000 feet, and 6,000,000 cubic yards of earth must be hauled 3,000+ feet. During a 20-month project the monthly quotas are, respectively, 200,000 cubic yards, 900,000 cubic yards, and 300,000 cubic yards. The construction manager would like to exceed his quotas, if possible.

6. *Budget goal:* The construction manager has a monthly budget of $350,000 for this equipment, and would like to run under budget.

7. *Ratio of scrapers to bulldozers goal:* There are various techniques involved in earth-moving. Sometimes, as is assumed in this case, scrapers can move into an area, drop their bin, and pick up their load all by themselves. However, unpleasant surprises may be found once the top few feet of soil have been removed. The underlying soil may not behave as test boring indicated it would. This could force the construction manager to adopt a push-pull method of moving earth using both scrapers and bulldozers. The construction manager imposes this constraint because he wants the flexibility of being able to immediately convert to the push-pull technique, even though he currently sees no need for implementing that strategy. A manager would resort to the push-pull method if the soil becomes too tough for a scraper to operate by itself. In this method a bulldozer is teamed with a scraper. As the scraper drops its bin to pick up a load, the bulldozer comes in behind and pushes the scraper along. When the scraper is full, it raises its bin and the bulldozer backs off. All available sizes of bulldozers have more than enough horsepower to push a scraper through the loading process. Also, it takes a scraper just as long to gather a load as it does to dump it, so there will be just one ratio of bulldozers to scrapers. The ratio is one bulldozer for every four scrapers.

CHAPTER QUESTIONS

11.1 What are the decision variables for this LGP problem? Define each.

11.2 What is the LGP formulation for this project management problem? Define the meaning of each of your deviational variables.

11.3 What assumptions are you making in using LGP to formulate this problem situation?

11.4 What is the optimal solution for this problem?

11.5 Can the model developed above be useful in modeling other projects? Prepare a brief explanation on what modeling elements and parameters may be changed in the Kansas-Osage Waterway Project model to adapt it for other project situations.

SELECTED REFERENCES

Bazaraa, M.S., and Bonzaker, A., "A Linear Goal Programming Model for Developing Economics with an Illustration from the Agricultural Sector in Egypt," *Management Science,* Vol. 27, No. 4, (April, 1981), pp. 442–447.

Kwak, N.K., and Schniederjans, M.J., "A Goal Programming Model for Improved Transportation Problem Solutions," *Omega,* Vol. 7, No. 4, (1979), pp. 367–370.

Lawrence, K.D., and Burbridge, J.J., "A Multiple Goal Programming Model for the Coordinated Production and Logistics Planning," *International Journal of Production Research,* Vol. 14, No. 2, (1976), pp. 237–244.

12

Crawford Computer Corporation

The Crawford Computer Corporation (CCC) manufactures "floppy" computer diskettes for computer software wholesalers. The diskettes are placed in boxes of 10 each and sold to the wholesalers who place their own labels on the boxes for brand recognition purposes. The CCC owns three production plants located in the state of California. Their location and weekly production capacity in boxes are presented in Exhibit 12.1. The wholesalers who purchase CCC diskettes are spread throughout the United States. The wholesalers' locations and weekly contractual requirements are presented in Exhibit 12.2.

CCC owns trucks for shipping their product to their customers. Unfortunately, the competitiveness in computer diskette sales requires a low profit margin on the product. In some of their markets, the transportation costs eliminate the profit altogether. Minimizing the costs of transporting their produce has become a very important priority for CCC. In August of 1981, no distribution plan or schedule

Exhibit 12.1 Plant Locations and Production Capabilities

Location	Weekly Production Capacity (boxes)
Sacramento	150,000
Salinas	250,000
San Diego	300,000

177

Exhibit 12.2 Wholesaler Locations and Product Demand

Location	Weekly Product Demand (boxes)
Boston	120,000
New York	80,000
Miami	100,000
St. Louis	50,000
Los Angeles	250,000
Seattle	50,000
Denver	50,000

was being used to minimize cost. The Vice President of Operations would simply call the three plant managers and tell them how many boxes of diskettes should be shipped to which wholesaler based on orders he would receive.

In August of 1981, Gale Crawford, President of the Crawford Computer Corporation, hired a consultant to advise her on establishing a cost minimizing distribution management policy. Stacy Shannon, the consultant, gathered the relevant transportation cost, supply and demand information to model the distribution network between the three CCC production plants and the seven wholesalers. In the process of developing the model, Stacy found that President Crawford had several additional goals besides transportation cost minimization. Her goals listed in their order of importance are as follows:

1. Allocate all of the weekly production capacity to satisfy the wholesaler demand. (Reason: Demand always outstrips supply in this expanding micro computer market.)

2. Limit the Miami wholesaler to obtaining all of the products from just the San Diego production plant. (Reason: The President knew that quality control in the San Diego plant was better than in the other two plants, and the Miami wholesaler had recently complained about poor product quality.)

3. Prohibit, if possible, shipments between the Sacramento plant and the St. Louis wholesaler. (Reason: Local union contracts were up for renegotiation and a sympathy strike by CCC truck drivers was possible.)

4. Prohibit, if possible, shipments between the Sacramento plant and the Los Angeles wholesaler. (Reason: same as 3 above.)

5. Minimize transportation costs.

The transportation costs per box of diskettes between each of the plants and wholesalers were obtained from corporation accountants. This cost information is presented in Exhibit 12.3. The estimated average weekly transportation cost, based on 700,000 boxes shipped, was $70,000. From this information, Stacy developed an LGP model in December, 1981, to optimize the distribution of diskettes from the plants to the wholesalers in accordance with President Crawford's goals. The resulting LGP model is presented in Exhibit 12.4. The explanation and presentation of the model and the resulting solution was made in January of 1982. In attendance at the meeting were Stacy, President Crawford, and the Vice President of Operations, Bill Crawford (no relation to the president). Bill Crawford had not met Stacy until the day of the presentation in January, but as the head of operations he was directly responsible for using and implementing the consultant's recommendations, once accepted by CCC. Bill raised several questions about the logic behind the ordering of the president's goals in the model. The vice president felt that minimizing transportation costs should, after total production capacity was allocated, be the second most important goal to work towards. He felt that customer quality control opinions and potential labor problems were less important than the cost minimization goal. The president responded by implying that Bill was more concerned with his merit bonus (which was tied to cost reduction in the operations) than the corporation's overall success in the marketplace. The president overruled the vice president, and Stacy's recommendations were accepted in total by the president. Bill Crawford was then instructed to implement Stacy's recommended distribution schedule as soon as possible.

In July of 1982, Stacy was invited to visit CCC again by President Crawford. The consultant was asked to prepare a "before and after" cost report for an upcoming Board of Directors meeting. The report was to be used by President Crawford to

---

Exhibit 12.3 Transportation Cost Per Box Between the Production Plants and Wholesalers

	Plant		
Wholesaler	Sacramento	Salinas	San Diego
Boston	.07 (x_{11})*	.07 (x_{12})	.09 (x_{13})
New York	.08 (x_{21})	.10 (x_{22})	.12 (x_{23})
Miami	.12 (x_{31})	.10 (x_{32})	.09 (x_{33})
St. Louis	.06 (x_{41})	.05 (x_{42})	.07 (x_{43})
Los Angeles	.02 (x_{51})	.02 (x_{52})	.01 (x_{53})
Seattle	.03 (x_{61})	.04 (x_{62})	.05 (x_{63})
Denver	.05 (x_{71})	.04 (x_{72})	.06 (x_{73})

*These are the decision variables for the transportation model. Each x_{ij} represents the number of boxes of computer diskettes to be shipped to each ith wholesaler from each jth plant.

179

Exhibit 12.4 LGP model of the Crawford Computer Corporation

Minimize: $Z = P_1(d_1^- + \ldots + d_{10}^- + d_1^+ + \ldots + d_{10}^+)$
$+ P_2(d_{11}^+ + d_{12}^+) + P_3 d_{13}^+ + P_4 d_{14}^+ + P_5 d_{15}^+$

subject to:

$$x_{11} + x_{12} + x_{13} + d_1^- - d_1^+ = 120$$
$$x_{21} + x_{22} + x_{23} + d_2^- - d_2^+ = 80$$
$$x_{31} + x_{32} + x_{33} + d_3^- - d_3^+ = 100$$
$$x_{41} + x_{42} + x_{43} + d_4^- - d_4^+ = 50$$
$$x_{51} + x_{52} + x_{53} + d_5^- - d_5^+ = 250$$
$$x_{61} + x_{62} + x_{63} + d_6^- - d_6^+ = 50$$
$$x_{71} + x_{72} + x_{73} + d_7^- - d_7^+ = 50$$
$$x_{11} + x_{21} + x_{31} + x_{41} + x_{51} + x_{61} + x_{71} + d_8^- - d_8^+ = 150$$
$$x_{12} + x_{22} + x_{32} + x_{42} + x_{52} + x_{62} + x_{72} + d_9^- - d_9^+ = 250$$
$$x_{13} + x_{23} + x_{33} + x_{43} + x_{53} + x_{63} + x_{73} + d_{10}^- - d_{10}^+ = 300$$
$$x_{31} \qquad\qquad - d_{11}^+ = 0$$
$$x_{32} \qquad\qquad - d_{12}^+ = 0$$
$$x_{41} \qquad\qquad - d_{13}^+ = 0$$
$$x_{51} \qquad\qquad - d_{14}^+ = 0$$
$$.07x_{11} + .07x_{12} + \ldots + .06x_{73} \qquad - d_{15}^+ = 0$$

and $x_{ij}, d_i^-, d_i^+ \geq 0$ and integer

justify the use of an outside consultant as well as to demonstrate her administrative competence at the Board meeting.

Despite the passage of time, Stacy found that her distribution schedule had only partially been implemented. Some weeks the plan had been used and some weeks not. In fact, total transportation costs in the first six months of 1982 had actually gone up by five percent over the last six months of 1981. Stacy tried several times to meet with Vice President Bill Crawford, but he always seemed to be out of his office. Stacy finally asked President Crawford to set up a meeting so she could present the results of her "before and after" cost report to both the president and vice president. The meeting was set for the first week in August.

CHAPTER QUESTIONS

12.1 Should Stacy Shannon have met Vice President Crawford before the January 1982 meeting? Why?

12.2 How could Stacy have used sensitivity analysis to clarify the value of Bill Crawford's reordering of the LGP model goals? Demonstrate by performing a sensitivity analysis and by explaining what advantages and disadvantages exist in the differing solutions.

12.3 What should Stacy Shannon say at the August, 1982 meeting? Design an itinerary and state the way in which you would deal with the issues listed on the itinerary.

SELECTED REFERENCES

Kwak, N.K., and Schniederjans, M.J., "A Goal Programming Model for Improved Transportation Problem Solutions," *OMEGA,* Vol. 7, No. 4, (1979), pp. 367–370.

Lee, S.M.; Green, G.I.; and Kim, C.I., "A Multiple Criteria Model for the Location-Allocation Problem," *Computers and Operations Research,* Vol. 8, No. 1, (1981), pp. 1–8.

Schniederjans, M.J.; Kwak, N.K.; and Helmer, M.C., "An Application of Goal Programming to Resolve a Site Location Problem," *Interfaces.* Vol. 12, No. 3, (June, 1982), p. 65–72.

13
Boswell
Advertising Consultants
Corporation

In April of 1983, the President of Boswell Advertising Consultants Corporation (BACC), Nettie Bowen, was contacted by Harold Glenwood, the Marketing Director of Carlson Manufacturing. Carlson Manufacturing develops and produces a number of toy products for sale in the United States and Canada. Carlson Manufacturing recently developed a new product which they plan to test market in Kansas City, Missouri. To insure the best possible market response to their new product, the best advertising firm was to be employed to develop an advertising campaign for the new product.

HAROLD GLENWOOD: Nettie, we need an ad campaign for our new Squeak-o Toy. In the past, we have developed our own new product campaigns with mixed results. We felt this time we would like a local firm familiar with the Kansas City area, such as yourself, to advise us on how we can best allocate our advertising budget. The advertising budget for the new product during its first month of market introduction is approximately $1,000,000. This budget is just for the Kansas City area. What we want BACC to do is advise us on how to allocate the budget over the various types of media available in Kansas City. The following are restrictions that must be observed in the budget allocation recommendations BACC develops for us:

1. Some printed media, such as newspapers, must be used.

2. Some radio commercials must be used.

3. Commercials on radio and television must be equally spread between day and night.

183

4. The ad campaign must begin in July, 1983.

5. We will develop and provide all printed and commercial ads.

Carlson Manufacturing has several goals in the Kansas City advertising campaign. We would like to:

1. *Maximize the potential purchase families reached:* We want our product to be introduced to the largest number of families as possible. They may not buy the toy, but everybody will be talking about it.

2. *Maximize potential unit sales:* We want to sell the toy. The market response in unit sales in Kansas City will help us determine a market forecast, set production levels and determine our pricing strategy for the new product.

3. *Maximize the cost/benefit of advertising efforts:* We want to get the most market response we can for our advertising budget dollars.

We know the BACC is the best ad consultant group in Kansas City and that's why we contacted you first. Are you interested in this project?

NETTIE BOWEN: Yes, BACC will be glad to handle this project for Carlson Manufacturing. We will need some sample copies of the new toy product and BACC will need a retainer equal to our fee of 10 percent of the advertising budget. We will have your advertising campaign finished by mid-June.

President Bowen began researching this problem by determining the media alternatives available to Carlson Manufacturing. Carlson Manufacturing would only have from mid-June (i.e., when BACC presented their media suggestions) to the beginning of July (i.e., stated introduction of new product) to purchase media spots. This time restriction limits the type of media availability. In Exhibit 13.1 the types of media available to Carlson are presented. The competitive nature of obtaining commercial spots on radio and television as well as newspaper ads and billboard space restrict not only the type of media available but also the maximum availability within the introductory first month. President Bowen found that each type of media had already sold most of their commercial space. The maximum ad spots available during the month of July are presented in Exhibit 13.1 along with their respective costs and media agent forecasts on potential purchase families reached.

Having determined the media available to promote the new toy, President Bowen, with the aid of her staff, developed forecasts on potential unit sales. These forecasts were developed based on the new product's characteristics, the track record of similar products introduced in the Kansas City area, and the potential purchase-families-reached estimates provided by the media agents. These potential unit sales are also presented in Exhibit 13.1.

A number of media cost-saving opportunities existed for BACC because of their media agent contacts. These opportunities are as follows:

Exhibit 13.1 Advertising Media Alternatives

Agent	Type of Media	Potential Purchase Families Reached	Cost Per Advertisement ($)	Maximum ads available in July	Potential Unit Sales in July
KXON TV, Inc.	30 sec., day commercial	30,000	1500	20	1,000
KXON TV, Inc.	15 sec., day commercial	10,000	900	5	400
KXON TV, Inc.	30 sec., night commercial	50,000	3000	10	2,500
KXON TV, Inc.	15 sec., night commercial	25,000	1500	5	1,000
KXXN TV, Inc.	30 sec., day commercial	28,000	1400	25	1,200
KXXN TV, Inc.	15 sec., day commercial	12,000	1000	20	500
KXXN TV, Inc.	30 sec., night commercial	56,000	3200	10	3,000
KXXN TV, Inc.	15 sec., night commercial	24,000	1400	5	1,000
Post Dispatch, Inc.	full page ad, week day	75,000	8000	4	4,500
Post Dispatch, Inc.	half page ad, week day	35,000	5000	4	2,000
Globe Daily, Inc.	half page ad, week day	40,000	5500	10	2,300
KXXN Radio, Inc.	15 sec., day commercial	6,000	800	50	300
KONN Radio, Inc.	30 sec., day commercial	12,000	1000	100	700
KONN Radio, Inc.	15 sec., day commercial	8,000	1000	50	400
KONN Radio, Inc.	30 sec., night commercial	18,000	1200	50	1,000
KONN Radio, Inc.	15 sec., night commercial	10,000	1200	20	400
Board Signs, Inc.	one month billboard	5,000	600	5	300

1. KXON TV, Inc. offered a 10 percent discount on all of their commercial spots if BACC purchased at least 15, 30-second commercials and 5, 15-second commercials during July.

2. KXXN TV, Inc. offered a 15 percent discount on all commercial spots if BACC purchased at least 30 commercial TV spots and 10 commercial radio spots from KXXN Radio, Inc. during July.

3. KONN Radio, Inc. offered a 5 percent discount on all commercial spots if BACC purchased 45 daytime spots during July.

CHAPTER QUESTIONS

13.1 Should President Bowen consider the restrictions Harold Glenwood placed on the budget allocation recommendations as goals? If so, at what priority level should they be placed?

13.2 Can you formulate this media selection decision situation as an LGP model? If so, provide the formulations.

13.3 Can you formulate this problem using variables that define the optimal budget allocation per media, instead of determining the optimal number of media commercials? If so, define the decision variables in such a model.

13.4 Does your LGP model take into consideration the reduced exposure value for repeated media usage, audience overlap due to the use of different types of media and media timing (i.e., scheduling) considerations? What additional information would be necessary to include these important advertising management considerations in your model?

SELECTED REFERENCES

De Kluyver, C.A., "An Exploration of Various Goal Programming Formulations with Application to Advertising Media Scheduling," *Journal of the Operational Research Society,* Vol. 30, No. 2, (February, 1979), pp. 167–171.

De Kluyver, C.A., "Hard and Soft Constraints in Media Scheduling," *Journal of Advertising Research,* Vol. 18, No. 3, (June, 1978), pp. 27–31.

Keown, A.J., and Duncan, C.P., "Integer Goal Programming in Advertising Media Selection," *Decision Sciences,* Vol. 10, No. 4, (October, 1979), pp. 571–592.

14

Metropolis Center Hospital

In February of 1983, Frances Washington, the Director of Dietary Planning, met with the president of Metropolis Center Hospital (MCH) to discuss overall hospital dietary planning. President Sam West asked Frances to outline her planning efforts and discuss her use of models in dietary planning. Sam had recently encouraged several members of his staff, including Frances, to attend a series of lectures on the use of optimization models in health care. Sam also had recently purchased micro computers and ample software for each of his departments. Sam figured that the availability of computers and education might motivate staff members into using the computer and, in the long run, save them decision-making time, improve patient care and reduce MCH expenses.

PRESIDENT SAM WEST: Frances, it has been two months since you completed the series of lectures on health care optimization. Was the lecture series helpful and have you had occasion to use any of what you learned?

DIRECTOR FRANCES WASHINGTON: The series of lectures were most helpful. Currently, the MCH Dietary Department has been developing an LGP model to resolve the problems of planning appropriate intake levels of different food groups so as to provide a balanced diet for individual's special food restrictions. A number of conditions require control of the quantities for one or more constituents of the diet: obesity, diabetes, hypoglycemia and others. The method utilized in planning diets uses the average values for groups of foods. An exchange list is a grouping of foods in which the carbohydrate, protein, and fat values are about the same for

Exhibit 14.1 Food Exchange Lists for Calculating Diets

| Food Exchange | Measure | Quantity for One Exchange | | | | |
		Weight (gm)	Carbohydrate (gm)	Protein (gm)	Fat (gm)	Calories
Milk	8 oz.	240	12	8	10	170
Vegetables–A	As desired	—	2	—	—	10
Vegetables–B	½ cup	100	7	2	—	36
Fruit	Varies	—	10	—	—	40
Bread	Varies	—	15	2	—	68
Meat	1 oz.	30	—	7	5	73
Fat	1 teaspoon	5	—	—	5	45

the items listed. A sample of a food exchange list is presented in Exhibit 14.1. The foods are divided into seven groups, according to their composition. These food exchange lists are easy for people to use at home or elsewhere. The LGP model we are developing will be used to plan for the number of food exchanges needed to fulfill a multi-objective diet.

In past applications to food problems, linear programming was used to select an optimal nutritional mix at the least cost. The lower level of each food group requirement is usually specified in the food group constraints. There has been a tendency for solutions to show a gross imbalance of some nutrients in applications of linear programming where only minimum levels of nutrient requirements are set. Harmful effects can take place when nutrients have been taken in excess. For example, an excess of vitamin A may cause dry skin, hair loss, and sore lips.

The objective of past linear programming models was to minimize some type of food intake while meeting certain daily dietary requirements. Let me illustrate with an example.

Linear programming can be used to determine the optimal number of each food exchange needed in a reducing diet for a 130-pound person. The uni-objective is to minimize caloric intake subject to certain constraints. For a low-calorie diet the amount of protein desired is usually more than in a maintenance (normal) diet. This is because protein provides most people with a feeling of satisfaction (curbs the appetite). Protein also helps to correct the greater losses of muscle tissue that occur during reducing. The "Meat" group is the most important provider of protein. The amount of protein required in the diet is equal to five-tenths of a gram per pound of body weight. The amount of carbohydrates included in one's diet should not be less than 100 grams to provide for the efficient oxidation of fats. A minimum level of fat intake is needed to provide for a balanced diet. It is said that 30 percent of one's total caloric intake, or around 40 grams at minimum, should be alloted to fats. Also, for variety and to insure adequate provision of all the vitamins and minerals required in one's daily diet, a minimum level of intake for each food exchange must be set.

The caloric minimization problem set up for solution by linear programming is as follows:

Minimize: $Z = 40x_1 + 170x_2 + 10x_3 + 36x_4 + 68x_5 + 73x_6 + 45x_7$
(Calorie Intake)

subject to:

$$8x_2 + 2x_4 + 2x_5 + 7x_6 \geqslant 65 \quad \text{(Required Protein Level)}$$
$$10x_2 + 5x_6 + 5x_7 \geqslant 40 \quad \text{(Minimum Level of Fat Intake)}$$
$$10x_1 + 12x_2 + 2x_3 + 7x_4 + 15x_5 \geqslant 100 \quad \text{Carbohydrate Restriction)}$$
$$x_1 \geqslant 3 \quad \text{(Food Exchange)}$$
$$x_2 \geqslant 2 \quad \text{(Food Exchange)}$$
$$x_3 \geqslant 3 \quad \text{(Food Exchange)}$$
$$x_4 \geqslant 1 \quad \text{(Food Exchange)}$$
$$x_5 \geqslant 2 \quad \text{(Food Exchange)}$$
$$x_6 \geqslant 6 \quad \text{(Food Exchange)}$$
$$x_7 \geqslant 3 \quad \text{(Food Exchange)}$$

and
$$x_j \geqslant 0$$

The solution to this LP problem is presented in Exhibit 14.2. The conditions set by the constraints are met, as are all the nutritional requirements. There is no flexibility in which to change any of the conditions in the problem without causing the solution to deviate greatly from the nutritional standards set. The caloric contribution of each food exchange group is unchangeable. In other words, the amount

Exhibit 14.2   Solutions for Dietary Problem

Model Variable	Description	Solutions LP*	LGP**	Unit of Measure
x_1	Milk	3.000	3.000	8 ounces
x_2	Vegetable–A	2.000	2.094	any
x_3	Vegetable–B	3.000	3.000	cup
x_4	Fruit	1.427	1.000	any
x_5	Bread	2.000	2.125	any
x_6	Meat	6.020	6.000	1 ounce
x_7	Fat	3.000	1.679	1 teaspoon

*Z = 1257.917 Calories
**$P_1 = P_2 = P_3 = 0$ and $P_4 = 0.218$

of calories contained in four ounces of meat or one meat exchange is not going to change. For a different type of diet (i.e., fat restricted, milk restricted, etc.), the objective function and constraints would change. One problem with using linear programming is in over-constraining the problem so that there is no feasible solution.

Taking the same problem and applying the LGP technique will allow multiple goals to be set. The caloric content in the objective function will be replaced by the deviations of different food groups and exchanges from their requirement levels. The goals in this problem are as follows:

P_1 = To achieve an intake of 1200 calories

P_2 = To minimize the underutilization of 65 grams of protein in the diet

P_3 = To minimize the underutilization of 100 grams of carbohydrates and 40 grams of fat included in the diet

P_4 = To minimize the overutilization of the number of food exchanges specified in the diet

The LGP model formulation is as follows:

Minimize: $Z = P_1(d_1^- + d_1^+) + P_2(d_2^-) + P_3(d_3^- + d_4^-)$
$$+ P_4(d_5^+ + d_6^+ + d_7^+ + d_8^+ + d_9^+ + d_{10}^+ + d_{11}^+)$$

subject to:

$$40x_1 + 170x_2 + 10x_3 + 36x_4 + 68x_5 + 73x_6 + 45x_7 + d_1^- - d_1^+ = 1200$$
$$8x_2 + 2x_4 + 2x_5 + 7x_6 + d_2^- - d_2^+ = 65$$
$$10x_2 + 5x_6 + 5x_7 + d_3^- - d_3^+ = 40$$
$$10x_1 + 12x_2 + 2x_3 + 7x_4 + 15x_5 + d_4^- - d_4^+ = 100$$
$$x_1 + d_5^- - d_5^+ = 3$$
$$x_2 + d_6^- - d_6^+ = 2$$
$$x_3 + d_7^- - d_7^+ = 3$$
$$x_4 + d_8^- - d_8^+ = 1$$
$$x_5 + d_9^- - d_9^+ = 2$$
$$x_6 + d_{10}^- - d_{10}^+ = 6$$
$$x_7 + d_{11}^- - d_{11}^+ = 3$$

and $x_j, d_i^-, d_i^+ \geq 0$

Due to the structure of the goals which may be over or underachieved, this LGP model formulation is more solution-flexible than the linear programming problem formulation. The solution to the LGP problem is presented in Exhibit 14.2.

Comparing the results of the LGP model with those of the linear programming model, it can be seen that LGP provides a slightly better solution. The percentage of deviation from the objectives were less in the LGP model. Total calories in the LGP model were 1200 while the linear programming model's solution results in

1257.917 calories. The fourth priority is the only goal that is not met, but its total deviation from the food exchange priority group is only .218.

It is my belief, Sam, that the LGP model we developed and illustrated here can generate a solution that will satisfy all four goals. As yet, we are continuing to work with the model by altering the goal constraints to determine if all of the goals can be fully satisfied.

CHAPTER QUESTIONS

14.1 Based on your understanding of the four priority levels, can you suggest restructuring the priorities to fully satisfy all four priority levels?

14.2 How many different problem formulation combinations are possible given the four priority levels in the LGP model?

14.3 Solve the problem formulations where the ordering of the priorities are $P_2P_1P_3P_4$, $P_3P_2P_1P_4$, and $P_4P_2P_3P_1$ using LGP sensitivity analysis. Do any of these models fully satisfy the four priority levels in the model? Are any of these model's solutions better than the P_1, P_2, P_3 and P_4 ordering?

SELECTED REFERENCES

Anderson, A.M., and Earle, M.D., "Diet Planning in the Third World by Linear and Goal Programming," *Journal of the Operational Research Society,* Vol. 34, No. 1, (January, 1983), pp. 9–13.

Arthur, J.L., and Lawrence, K.D., "A Multiple Goal Blending Problem," *Computer and Operations Research,* Vol. 7, No. 3, (1980), pp. 215–224.

Neely, W.P.; Sellers, J.; and North, R.M., "Goal Programming Priority Sensitivity Analysis: An Application in Natural Resource Decision Making Processes," *Interfaces,* Vol. 10, No. 5, (October, 1980), pp. 83–89.

15
Weinstein Educational Institute

The Weinstein Educational Institute (WEI) is a degree-granting higher education institute that is comprised of six divisions: Business & Consumer Science, Human Development, Humanities, Musical Arts, Nursing, and Science & Mathematics. Each of these divisions offers a fully accredited baccalaureate degree.

In January of 1982, Ashlyn Bomberg, an education planning consultant, was invited by the President of WEI, Fred Lee, to the 1982–83 Planning Committee meeting. In attendance at the meeting were all of the division heads as well as the vice presidents of finance and personnel.

Fred Lee started the meeting by introducing Ms. Bomberg and stated her role as a planning consultant. He then announced that enrollment projections in all of the six divisions of the institute indicated a significant increase over the current 1981–82 school year. President Lee felt that a professional consultant might provide useful information on potential staffing needs for the next year.

During the course of the 1982–83 Planning Committee meeting, Carla took the following notes:

VICE PRESIDENT OF PERSONNEL: A sufficient number of faculty exist in the labor market to satisfy any demand requirements WEI might need for the 1982–83 school year. Minimum faculty requirements by division and by education level are presented in Exhibit 15.1. The "minimum faculty requirements" are the least number of personnel required before the accreditation of the institute is placed in jeopardy. All faculty have sufficient skills to teach any course in their respective curriculums.

Exhibit 15.1 Minimum Faculty Requirements for 1982–83 School Year

| | Education Level | | | |
Division	Full Professor	Associate Professor	Assistant Professor	Instructors
Business & Consumer Science	1	1	3	4
Human Development	1	1	2	4
Humanities	2	1	3	5
Musical Arts	1	1	2	3
Nursing	1	1	2	3
Science & Mathematics	1	1	3	3

VICE PRESIDENT OF FINANCE: The total budgeted payroll for faculty projected for the 1982–83 school year is four million dollars. The specific salaries each type of faculty receives is presented in Exhibit 15.2. The salaries are uniform within each of the six education levels.

PRESIDENT: The following are the goals, in their order of importance, regarding our 1982–83 staffing decisions:

1. *Accreditation:* To maintain school accreditation, we should have an equal number of terminally degreed faculty (i.e., full, associate, and assistant professors) and non-terminally degreed faculty (i.e., instructors) by division. We should also have no more than a 1 to 20, faculty to student ratio. Projected total enrollment by division is presented in Exhibit 15.3.

2. *Adequate course offerings:* Each student, on average, takes 15 credit hours per semester. Each faculty member is expected to teach three, three-credit-hour

Exhibit 15.2 Faculty Salaries for the 1982–83 School Year

| | Education Level | | | |
Division	Full Professor	Associate Professor	Assistant Professor	Instructor
Business & Consumer Science	36	30	27	18
Human Development	32	27	22	15
Humanities	30	25	20	12
Musical Arts	30	25	20	12
Nursing	36	32	29	18
Science & Mathematics	30	25	20	12

194

Exhibit 15.3 Projected Student Enrollment for the 1982–83 School Year

Division	Student Enrollment	Increase Over Prior Year
Business & Consumer Science	400	200
Human Development	400	150
Humanities	580	50
Musical Arts	280	50
Nursing	280	60
Science & Mathematics	280	60

courses per semester, with a maximum of twenty students in each three-credit-hour course. WEI should offer an adequate number of courses to permit each student to take at least five, three-credit-hour courses per semester.

3. *Satisfy minimum faculty requirements:* To insure each of the divisions future success, the minimum faculty requirements should be satisfied in total and by level of education.

4. *Growth in faculty:* Beyond the minimum number of faculty required, projected student enrollment will necessitate the addition of new faculty. The addition of new faculty should be differentially weighted by the relative increase in students by division.

5. *Maximize full professor hiring:* The more senior or experienced the faculty member, the easier accreditation is to achieve. During the 1982–83 school year the Business & Consumer Science, Humanities and Nursing Divisions will be up for accreditation review. It is desirable to hire as many full professors in these divisions as possible.

6. *Minimize costs:* WEI should, wherever possible, minimize operating expenses. Since salaries represent 80 percent of total operating expenses, minimizing salaries is obviously very important.

After the committee meeting, Ms. Bomberg met with President Lee to discuss her consulting job with WEI. In the discussion that ensued, Ms. Bomberg agreed to determine the optimal number of faculty to hire for the 1982–83 school year on the condition that she be paid for her effort by receiving 50 percent of the salary funds under the four million budgeted allocation.

CHAPTER QUESTIONS

15.1 What is the LGP formulation for the WEI problem situation?

15.2 What are the optimal faculty hiring requirements for the 1982–83 school year?

15.3 What will Ashlyn Bomberg be paid for her consulting efforts?

SELECTED REFERENCES

Joiner, C., "Academic Planning Through the Goal Programming Model," *Interfaces,* Vol. 10, No. 4 (August, 1980), pp. 86–92.

Schroeder, R.G., "Resource Planning in University Management by Goal Programming," *Operations Research,* Vol. 22, No. 4, (January/April, 1974), pp. 700–710.

Walters, A.; Mangold, J.; and Haran, E., "A Comprehensive Planning Model for Long-Range Academic Strategies," *Management Science,* Vol. 22, No. 7, (March, 1976), pp. 727–738.

16

United States Air Force Antisubmarine Allocation Plan

The Chief Executive Officer, Colonel Freeman, of the Department of Operations Research of the United States Air Force (USAF) was requested by his commander to devise an aircraft allocation plan in the Gulf of Mexico. In Exhibit 16.1 we can see that the Gulf of Mexico is divided into 30 quadrants, each consisting of several thousand square miles of gulf waters. Each of these quadrants require surveillance by USAF aircraft to prevent the possibility of sneak attack by one of our nation's enemies. In particular, Colonel Freeman was requested to develop a plan that would allocate specialized USAF antisubmarine aircraft to each quadrant listed in Exhibit 16.1. The available specialized aircraft and their base locations are listed in Exhibit 16.2.

Colonel Freeman's commander set down the following goals for the resulting allocation plan to achieve:

1. Meet minimum aircraft requirements in each quadrant, during each shift.

2. Allocate aircraft in accordance to the historic probabilistic occurance of enemy submarine activity.

3. Maintain a 24-hour surveillance plan.

4. Minimize traveling distance to and from each airbase.

To begin modeling the required allocation plan, Colonel Freeman examined the specialized aircraft to determine if these jet planes possessed any special limitations on the model. He found that any of the aircraft, regardless of the base of origin, could reach any of the quadrants and patrol for up to eight hours. For model planning

Exhibit 16.1 Gulf of Mexico and Quadrant Definitions

	1	2	3	4		
5	6	7	8	9	10	
11	12	13	14	15	16	17	18
19	20	21	22	23	24	25	26
	27	28	29	30		

$\triangle$1 = Lackland AFB: San Antonio, TX
$\triangle$2 = England AFB: Alexandria, LA
$\triangle$3 = English AFB: Panamaha Beach, FL

purposes, he decided to model three shifts each day. Research also indicated that sufficient service crews are available to provide necessary manpower requirements. Three airforce bases (Lackland, England and English) were assigned the specialized aircraft. The assignment of aircraft to each base was determined on each base's ability to provide facility and mechanical support. No reassignment of aircraft between the three airforce bases was possible.

Each airforce base was assigned a mission to patrol a given set of quadrants. The quadrant assignments are presented in Exhibit 16.2. As can be seen, there is some overlapping of quadrant assignments. Colonel Freeman found that this resulted in some quadrants receiving too much surveillance. The needless duplication of

Exhibit 16.2 Available Aircraft and Quadrant Assignments

Airforce Base	Aircraft Available	Quadrants Assigned to Each Base
Lackland (TX)	108	5,6,7,11,12,13,14,19,20,21,22,27,28
England (LA)	120	1,2,3,4,6,7,8,9,13,14,15,16,22,23,28,29
English (FL)	108	8,9,10,15,16,17,18,23,24,26,29,30

effort also, unfortunately, reduced coverage in other quadrants below the minimum of three aircraft.

Colonel Freeman next researched past Gulf of Mexico enemy submarine sightings during the last 10 years. By tallying the sightings by quadrant, the historical probability of submarine sightings could be determined. These probabilities are presented in Exhibit 16.3. Since enemy submarines had been repeatedly sighted in some

Exhibit 16.3

Quadrant	Probability of Submarine Occurance (percent)	One-Way Trip Distance Between Each Quadrant and Each AFB (miles)		
		Lackland	England	English
1	3	475	200	575
2	1	550	225	475
3	6	650	250	400
4	1	750	300	300
5	6	350	225	700
6	1	450	275	600
7	1	550	275	500
8	7	650	300	425
9	1	750	350	325
10	1	850	400	275
11	2	250	375	800
12	7	350	350	725
13	6	450	325	475
14	1	550	400	525
15	5	650	400	475
16	4	750	400	400
17	3	850	475	325
18	3	950	500	300
19	1	300	425	825
20	1	375	400	750
21	6	475	400	700
22	7	575	400	600
23	6	675	400	525
24	1	750	475	475
25	1	850	500	425
26	1	950	550	400
27	1	500	475	725
28	7	600	475	650
29	7	700	475	600
30	2	800	500	525

quadrants (i.e., usually those quadrants nearest to military installations or production facilities) chances are future sightings would also be in the same quadrants. By allocating an increased number of surveillance aircraft in those quadrants with the highest frequency of sightings, it would improve the likelihood of early submarine detection.

Next, Colonel Freeman examined the traveling distance the aircraft would be required to fly each day. He measured the distance between each of the 30 quadrants and each of the three airforce bases. The one-way trip traveling distance between the center of the quadrant and each airforce base is presented in Exhibit 16.3.

CHAPTER QUESTIONS

16.1 What, if any, additional information would you ask for to model this problem?

16.2 Can this problem be formulated as an LGP model? If so, formulate this problem into an LGP model.

16.3 What assumptions are required in your formulation?

SELECTED REFERENCES

Armstrong, R.D., and Cook, W.D., "Goal Programming Models for Assigning Search and Rescue Aircraft to Bases," *Journal of the Operational Research Society,* Vol. 30, No. 6, (June, 1979), pp. 555–561.

Mellichamp, J.M.; Dixon, W.L., Jr.; and Mitchell, S.L., "Ballistic Missile Defense Technology Management with Goal Programming," *Interfaces,* Vol. 10, No. 5, (October, 1980), pp. 68–75.

Sullivan, R.S., and Fitzsimmons, J.A., "Goal Programming—Model for Readiness and Optimal Redeployment of Resources," *Socio-Economic Planning Sciences,* Vol. 12, No. 5, (1978), pp. 215–220.

Appendix

A
LGP Macro
Computer Program

```
C
C          THIS PROGRAM IS A DUAL SIMPLEX GOAL PROGRAMMING
C          ALGORITHM.
C          IT HAS BEEN DIMENSIONED FOR 150 DECISION
C          VARIABLES, 150 CONSTRAINTS, AND 10 GOAL PRIORITY
           LEVELS.

           IMPLICIT REAL*8(A-H,P-Z)
           INTEGER*2 ITIME(15)
           COMMON NROW,NCOL,NVAR,NPRT,KTEST,ITER
           COMMON /R1/ BASIS(150,300)
           COMMON /R2/ VALC(11,300),VALB(11,150)
           COMMON /R3/ PRHS(150),RHS(150)
           COMMON /I1/ IBASIC(150),JCOL(300)
           CALL TIMDAT (ITIME, INTS(15))
           WRITE(6,888) ITIME(4),ITIME(5),ITIME(6)
      888  FORMAT(' MIN',I7,5X,'SEC',I4,5X,'TICKS',I5)
           WRITE(6,889) ITIME(7),ITIME(8),ITIME(9),ITIME(10)
      889  FORMAT (' CPU S',I4,3X,'CPU T',I5,5X,'IO S',I4,3X,'IO T',I5)
           CALL START
           CALL SIMPLX
           CALL FINISH
           CALL TIMDAT (ITIME,INTS(15))
           WRITE(6,888) ITIME(4),ITIME(5),ITIME(6)
           WRITE(6,889) ITIME(7),ITIME(8),ITIME(9),ITIME(10)
           STOP
           END
C
```

```
C            SUBROUTINE START READS INPUT AND INITIATES
C            WORKING MATRICES.
        SUBROUTINE START
        IMPLICIT REAL*8(A-H,P-Z)
        INTEGER*4 POS,NEG,END
        INTEGER*4 KSIGN
        INTEGER*2 E,G,L,B
        INTEGER*2 ISIGN
        COMMON NROW,NCOL,NVAR,NPRT,KTEST,ITER
        COMMON /R1/ BASIS(150,300)
        COMMON /R2/ VALC(11,300),VALB(11,150)
        COMMON /R3/ PRHS(150),RHS(150)
        COMMON /I1/ IBASIC(150),JCOL(300)
        DIMENSION ISIGN(300)
        DATA POS,NEG,END/'POS ','NEG ','END '/
        DATA E,G,L,B/'E ','G ','L ','B '/
        READ(5,*) NROW
        READ(5,*) NVAR
        READ(5,*) NPRT
        IF(NROW.LE.O) GO TO 91
        IF(NVAR.LE.O) GO TO 91
        IF(NPRT.LE.O) GO TO 91
        NCOL = NROW + NVAR
        DO 2 I=1,NROW
          DO 1 J=1,NCOL
          BASIS(I,J) = 0.0
          INDEX = J - NVAR
          IF(INDEX.EQ.I) BASIS(I,J) = 1.0
1       CONTINUE
        IND = I + NCOL
        IBASIC(I) = IND
2       CONTINUE
        DO 3 J=1,NCOL
        JCOL(J) = J
3       CONTINUE
        KEND = NPRT + 1
        DO 6 K=1,KEND
          DO 4 J=1,NCOL
          VALC(K,J) = 0.0
4       CONTINUE
          DO 5 I=1,NROW
          VALB(K,I) = 0.0
5       CONTINUE
6       CONTINUE
        KTEST=0
        READ(5,*) (ISIGN(I),I=1,NROW)
        DO 10 I=1,NROW
        IF (ISIGN(I).EQ.E) GO TO 7
```

```
       IF(ISIGN(I).EQ.G) GO TO 8
       IF(ISIGN(I).EG.L) GO TO 9
       IF(ISIGN(I).EQ.B) GO TO 10
       GO TO 92
 7     KTEST =1
       INDEX = I + NVAR
       VALB(1,I) = 1.0
       VALC(1,INDEX) = 1.0
       JCOL(INDEX) = 0
       GO TO 10
 8     INDEX = I + NVAR
       KTEST = 1
       VALC(1,INDEX) = 1.0
       JCOL(INDEX) = 0
       GO TO 10
 9     KTEST = 1
       VALB(1,I) = 1.0
10     CONTINUE
       IF(KTEST.EQ.1) NPRT = NPRT + 1
11     READ(5,*) KSIGN,I,K,WGT
       IF(KSIGN.EG.END) GO TO 13
       IF(KTEST.EQ.1) K = K + 1
       IF(KSIGN.EQ.POS) GO TO 12
       IF(KSIGN.NE.NEG) GO TO 94
       INDEX = I + NVAR
       VALC(K,INDEX) = WGT
       GO TO 11
12     CONTINUE
       VALB(K,I) = WGT
       GO TO 11
13     CONTINUE
15     READ(5,*) I,J,AIJ
       IF(I.EQ.O) GO TO 16
       BASIS(I,J) = AIJ
       GO TO 15
16     CONTINUE
       READ(5,*) (PRHS(I),I=1,NROW)
       DO 23 I=1,NROW
       IF(PRHS(I)) 20,21,22
20     GO TO 95
21     PRHS(I) = 1.0E-12
22     RHS(I) = -PRHS(I)
23     CONTINUE
       DO 31 J=1,NCOL
       IF(JCOL(J).NE.0) GO TO 31
         DO 30 I=1,NROW
         BASIS(I,J) = 0.0
30       CONTINUE
```

```
   31   CONTINUE
        RETURN
   91   WRITE(6,1091)
        STOP
   92   WRITE(6,1092)
        STOP
   94   WRITE(6,1094)
        STOP
   95   WRITE(6,1095)
        STOP
 1091   FORMAT (' NUMBER OF CONSTRAINTS, VARIABLES, OR
           PRIORITY LEVEL',/, ' IMPROPERLY ENTERED.')
 1092   FORMAT (' SIGN SYMBOL SOMETHING OTHER THAN E, G,
           L, OR B.')
 1094   FORMAT (' DEVIATION TO BE MINIMIZED NOT POS OR
           NEG')
 1095   FORMAT (' THIS PROGRAM REQUIRES NON-NEGATIVE
           RIGHT HAND SIDES.',/, 'MULTIPLY CONSTRAINT BY
           MINUS ONE.')
        END
C
C
C       THIS SUBROUTINE PERFORMS THE SIMPLEX OPERATION
C
        SUBROUTINE SIMPLX
        IMPLICIT REAL*8(A-H,P-Z)
        COMMON NROW,NCOL,NVAR,NPRT,KTEST,ITER
        COMMON /R1/ BASIS(150,300)
        COMMON /R2/ VALC(11,300),VALB(11,150)
        COMMON /R3/ PRHS(150),RHS(150)
        COMMON /I1/ IBASIC(150),JCOL(300)
        DIMENSION JFAIL(150),JPICK(300),ZVAL(11,300)
        KEND = NPRT + 1
        DO 16 J=1,NCOL
        JPICK(J) = KEND
   16   CONTINUE
        DO 18 J=1,NCOL
        DO 17 K=1,NPRT
        IF(VALC(K,J).LE.1.0E-10) GO TO 17
        JPICK(J) = K
   17   CONTINUE
   18   CONTINUE
        ITER = 0
    1   KEYROW = 0
        KEYCOL = 0
        KUNACH = 0
        DO 2 I=1,NROW
        JFAIL(I) = 1
    2   CONTINUE
```

```
C
C       IDENTIFY HIGHEST UNACHIEVED PRIORITY
C
        DO 4 K=1,NPRT
         DO 3 I=1,NROW
         IF(VALB(K,I).LE.1.0E-10) GO TO 3
         KUNACH = K
         GO TO 11
    3    CONTINUE
    4  CONTINUE
C
C          IDENTIFY THE MOST NEGATIVE RHS
C
   11  CONTINUE
       RMIN = -1.0E-10
       DO 12 I=1,NROW
       IF(RHS(I).GE.RMIN) GO TO 12
       IF(JFAIL(I).EQ.0) GO TO 12
       KEYROW = I
       RMIN = RHS(I)
   12  CONTINUE
C
C          IF KEYROW EQUALS 0, ALL RHS GREATER THAN OR
C          EQUAL TO 0
       IF(KEYROW.EQ.0) GO TO 30
C
C          PATH FOR NEGATIVE RIGHT HAND SIDE
C
       AIJ = 1.0E-8
       DO 25 M=1,KEND
       L = KEND - M + 1
         DO 24 J=1,NCOL
         IF(JCOL(J).EQ.0) GO TO 24
         IF(JPICK(J).LT.L) GO TO 24
         IF(BASIS(KEYROW,J).LE.AIJ) GO TO 24
         AIJ = BASIS(KEYROW,J)
         KEYCOL = J
   24    CONTINUE
       IF(KEYCOL.GT.0) GO TO 40
   25  CONTINUE
       JFAIL(KEYROW) = 0
       GO TO 11
C
C          PATH FOR NONNEGATIVE RIGHT HAND SIDE
C
   30  CONTINUE
       IF(KUNACH.EQ.0) GO TO 96
       KFIN = KUNACH
```

```
C
C              THE ZJ MATRIX IS DEVELOPED. SINCE BASIS IS
C              NEGATIVE OF CONVENTIONAL, ZJ CALCULATED WILL
C              BE NEGATIVE FOR FAVORABLE VARIABLES.
       DO 33 K=KUNACH,NPRT
         DO 32 J=1,NCOL
         ZVAL(K,J) = 0.0
         IF(JCOL(J).EQ.0) GO TO 32
         IF(JPICK(J).LT.KFIN) GO TO 32
            DO 31 I=1,NROW
            IF(VALB(K,I).LE.1.0E-10) GO TO 31
            IF(DABS(BASIS(I,J)).LE.1.0E-10) GO TO 31
            ZVAL(K,J) = ZVAL(K,J) + VALB(K,I)*BASIS(I,J)
31          CONTINUE
         ZVAL(K,J) = ZVAL(K,J) + VALC(K,J)
32       CONTINUE
33    CONTINUE
       ZVALUE = -1.0E-8
       DO 36 K=KUNACH,NPRT
         DO 35 J=1,NCOL
         IF(JCOL(J).EQ0) GO TO 35
         IF(JPICK(J).LT.KFIN) GO TO 35
         IF(ZVAL(K,J).GE.ZVALUE) GO TO 35
         IF(K.LE.KUNACH) GO TO 39
            M = K - 1
            DO 34 L=1,M
            IF(ZVAL(L,J).GE.1.0E-8) GO TO 35
34          CONTINUE
39       CONTINUE
       ZVALUE = ZVAL(K,J)
         KEYCOL = J
35       CONTINUE
       IF(KEYCOL.GT.0) GO TO 37
       KFIN = KFIN + 1
36    CONTINUE
       IF(KEYCOL.EQ.0) GO TO 97
37    THETA = 1.0E9
       DO 38 I=1,NROW
       IF(BASIS(I,KEYCOL).GE.-1.0E-10) GO TO 38
       IF(RHS(I).LE.-1.0E-10) GO TO 38
       IF(RHS(I).LE.1.0E-10) RHS(I) = 1.0E-10
       ZETA = -RHS(I)/BASIS(I,KEYCOL)
       IF(ZETA.GE.THETA) GO TO 38
       THETA = ZETA
       KEYROW = I
38    CONTINUE
       IF(KEYROW.GT.0) GO TO 40
       GO TO 97
```

```
C
C          SIMPLEX ROUTINE
C
40   CONTINUE
     PIV = BASIS(KEYROW,KEYCOL)
     DO 43 I=1,NROW
     IF(I.EQ.KEYROW) GO TO 43
     IF(DABS(BASIS(I,KEYCOL)).LE.1.0E-10) GO TO 43
     IF(DABS(RHS(KEYROW)).LE.1.0E-10) GO TO 41
     RHS(I) = RHS(I) − (RHS(KEYROW)/PIV)*BASIS(I,KEYCOL)
41     DO 42 J=1,NCOL
       IF(J.EQ.KEYCOL) GO TO 42
       IF(DABS(BASIS(KEYROW,J)).LE.1.0E-10) GO TO 42
     BASIS(I,J) = BASIS(I,J) − (BASIS(I,KEYCOL)/
      PIV)*BASIS(KEYROW,J)
42     CONTINUE
     BASIS(I,KEYCOL) = BASIS(I,KEYCOL)PIV
43   CONTINUE
     IF(DABS(RHS(KEYROW)).LE.1.0E-10) GO TO 44
     RHS(KEYROW) = − RHS(KEYROW)/PIV
44   CONTINUE
     DO 45 J=1,NCOL
     IF(J.EQ.KEYCOL) GO TO 45
     IF(DABS(BASIS(KEYROW,J)).LE.1.0E-10) GO TO 45
     BASIS(KEYROW,J) = − BASIS(KEYROW,J)/PIV
45   CONTINUE
     BASIS(KEYROW,KEYCOL) = 1/PIV
     INDEX = JCOL(KEYCOL)
     JCOL(KEYCOL) = IBASIC(KEYROW)
     IBASIC(KEYROW) = INDEX
     DO 46 K=1,NPRT
     DUMMY = VALB(K,KEYROW)
     IF(DUMMY.GE.1.0E-8) JPICK(KEYCOL) = K
     VALB(K,KEYROW) = VALC(K,KEYCOL)
     VALC(K,KEYCOL) = DUMMY
46   CONTINUE
     IF(KTEST.NE.1) GO TO 51
     IF(VALC(1,KEYCOL).EQ.0.0) GO TO 51
     JCOL(KEYCOL) = 0
     DO 50 I=1,NROW
     BASIS(I,KEYCOL) = 0.0
50   CONTINUE
51   CONTINUE
     ITER = ITER + 1
     GO TO 1
96   WRITE(6,1096)
97   RETURN
98   WRITE(6,1098)
```

```
                STOP
          1096  FORMAT(' ALL GOALS ACHIEVED')
          1098  FORMAT(' THE MODEL IS INFEASIBLE')
                END
C
C               THIS SUBROUTINE REPORTS THE FINAL SOLUTION.
C
                SUBROUTINE FINISH
                IMPLICIT REAL*8(A-H,P-Z)
                COMMON NROW,NCOL,NVAR,NPRT,KTEST,ITER
                COMMON /R1/ BASIS(150,300)
                COMMON /R2/ VALC(11,300),VALB(11,150)
                COMMON /R3/ PRHS(150),RHS(150)
                COMMON /I1/ IBASIC(150),JCOL(300)
                DIMENSION X(150),POSD(150),RNEGD(150)
C
C               THIS SECTION IDENTIFIES AND REPORTS THE VALUES OF
C                   ALL MODEL VARIABLES. REAL VARIABLES ARE
C                   REPORTED FIRST, THEN DEVIATIONAL VARIABLES
C
                DO 1 J=1,NVAR
                X(J) = 0.0
          1     CONTINUE
                DO 2 I=1,NROW
                POSD(I) = 0.0
                RNEGD(I) = 0.0
          2     CONTINUE
                DO 12 I=1,NROW
                IVAR = IBASIC(I)
                IF(IVAR.GT.NCOL) GO TO 11
                IF(IVAR.GT.NVAR) GO TO 10
                X(IVAR) = RHS(I)
                GO TO 12
          10    CONTINUE
                IND = IVAR - NVAR
                RNEGD(IND) = RHS(I)
                GO TO 12
          11    CONTINUE
                IND = IVAR - NCOL
                POSD(IND) = RHS(I)
          12    CONTINUE
                WRITE(6,1000) ITER
                WRITE(6,1001)
                WRITE(6,1002)
                DO 15 J=1,NVAR
                WRITE(6,1003) J,X(J)
          15    CONTINUE
                WRITE(6,1004)
```

```
        WRITE(6,1005)
        DO 16 I=1,NROW
        WRITE(6,1006) I,PRHS(I),POSD(I),RNEGD(I)
   16   CONTINUE
C
C       THIS SECTION PROVIDES A REPORT OF PRIORITY LEVEL
C          ACHIEVEMENT.
        WRITE(6,1013)
        KTOTAL = NPRT + 1
        DO 52 K=1,NPRT
        KVAL = KTOTAL - K
        M = KVAL
        IF(KTEST.EQ.1) M = KVAL - 1
        ZVALUE = 0.0
          D0 50 I=1,NROW
          IF(VALB(KVAL,I).LE.1.0E-10) GO TO 50
          IF(DABS(RHS(I)).LE.1.0E-10) GO TO 50
          ZVALUE = ZVALUE + VALB(KVAL,I)*RHS(I)
   50   CONTINUE
        IF(KTEST.EQ.0) GO TO 51
        IF(M.GT.0) GO TO 51
        WRITE(6,1015) ZVALUE
        GO TO 52
   51   WRITE(6,1014) M,ZVALUE
   52   CONTINUE
        RETURN
 1000   FORMAT (I6,'      ITERATIONS')
 1001   FORMAT (' DECISION VARIABLES')
 1002   FORMAT (/,' VARIABLE          VALUE')
 1003   FORMAT (3X,I5,3X,F15.5)
 1004   FORMAT (////,' ANALYSIS OF DEVIATIONS FROM GOALS')
 1005   FORMAT (/,' ROW',8X,'RHS-VALUE',10X,'POSITIVE
        DEVIATION',6X, 'NEGATIVE DEVIATION')
 1006   FORMAT (I4,3F20.5)
 1013   FORMAT (////,' ANALYSIS OF THE OBJECTIVE FUNCTION',//,'
        PRIORITY',9 X,'UNDERACHIEVEMENT')
 1014   FORMAT (I3,9X,F20.5)
 1015   FORMAT (' ARTIFICIAL',F20.5)
        END
```

Appendix

B

LGP Micro Computer Program

```
10      REM   SET UP PROBLEM AND FLAGS
20      HOME : CLEAR
30   D$ = CHR$ (4)
40      INPUT "DO YOU WANT INSTRUCTIONS? ";RP$
50      IF RP$ = "Y" THEN GOSUB 2150
60      IF RP$ = "Y" OR RP$ = "N" THEN GOTO 80
70      PRINT "Y OR N ONLY. TRY AGAIN.": GOTO 40
80      PRINT
90      INPUT "IS YOUR PROBLEM ALREADY ON FILE? ";RR$
100     IF RR$ = "Y" OR RR$ = "N" THEN GOTO 120
110     PRINT "Y OR N ONLY. TRY AGAIN.": GOTO 90
120     PRINT
130     INPUT "NAME YOUR PROBLEM. ";PR$
140     IF RR$ = "Y" THEN GOSUB 470
150     IF RR$ = "N" THEN GOSUB 790
160     IF RR$ = "N" THEN GOSUB 5740
170     IF RR$ = "N" THEN GOTO 230
180     IF RR$ = "Y" THEN INPUT "DO YOU WANT TO CHANGE IT?
        ";PF$
190     IF PF$ = "Y" THEN GOSUB 6020
200     IF PF$ = "Y" THEN GOTO 230
210     IF PF$ = "N" THEN GOTO 230
220     PRINT "Y OR N ONLY. TRY AGAIN.": GOTO 180
230     PRINT
240     INPUT "DO YOU WANT PRINTOUT? ";PO$
250     IF PO$ = "Y" THEN PRINT D$"PR#1": PRINT PR$: PRINT :
        PRINT D$"PR#0"
```

```
260     IF PO$ = "Y" THEN INPUT "INCLUDING TABLEAU? ";TB$: IF
            TB$ = "Y" THEN GOTO 300
270     IF PO$ = "Y" THEN GOTO 330
280     IF PO$ = "N" THEN GOTO 330
290     PRINT "Y OR N ONLY. TRY AGAIN.": GOTO 240
300     INPUT "(A)LL OR JUST (F)IRST? ";QQ$
310     IF QQ$ = "A" OR QQ$ = "F" THEN GOTO 330
320     PRINT "A OR F ONLY. TRY AGAIN.": GOTO 300
330     PRINT
340     GOSUB 2070
350     GOSUB 5480
360     IF QQ$ = "F" AND TC > 0 THEN GOTO 420
370     IF QQ$ = "F" THEN GOSUB 5620
380     IF QQ$ = "F" THEN GOSUB 5020
390     IF QQ$ = "F" THEN GOTO 420
400     IF QQ$ = "A" AND TC = 0 THEN GOSUB 5620
410     IF QQ$ = "A" THEN GOSUB 5020
420     GOSUB 3210
430     GOSUB 3710
440     GOSUB 4350
450     GOSUB 4690
460     GOTO 350
470     REM   READ FILE FROM DISK
480     PRINT D$"OPEN";PR$;",L300"
490     PRINT D$"READ";PR$;",R";0
500     INPUT NU: INPUT MC; INPUT P: INPUT N$
510     DIM A(MC,NU + (2 * MC) + 1),CZ(P,NU + (2 * MC) +
            1),C(NU + (2 * MC)),B(MC), WC(NU + (2 * MC)),WB(MC)
520     DIM N$(NU)
530     DIM Y$(MC),DI(NU + 2 * MC)
540     DIM DB(NU + 2 * MC)
550     FOR I = 1 TO MC
560     PRINT D$"READ";PR$;",R";I
570     FOR J = 1 TO NU + (2 * MC) + 1
580     INPUT A(I,J)
590     NEXT J
600     NEXT I
610   I = MC + 1
620     PRINT D$"READ";PR$;",R";I
630     FOR J = 1 TO NU + (2* MC)
640     INPUT C(J)
650     NEXT J
660   I = I + 1
670     PRINT D$"READ";PR$'",R";I
680     FOR J = 1 TO NU + (2 * MC)
690     INPUT WC(J)
700     NEXT J
710     IF N$ < > "Y" THEN GOTO 770
```

```
720   I = I + 1
730     PRINT D$"READ";PR$;",R";I
740     FOR J = 1 TO NU
750     INPUT N$(J)
760     NEXT J
770     PRINT D$"CLOSE";PR$;" "
780     RETURN
790     REM    DATA ENTRY ROUTINE
800     HOME : PRINT "READY TO ENTER DATA.": PRINT
810     PRINT : INPUT "NUMBER OF UNKNOWNS ";NU
820     PRINT
830     INPUT "WANT TO NAME VARIABLES? ";N$
840     PRINT
850     IF N$ = "N" THEN GOTO 920
860     IF N$ = "Y" THEN GOTO 880
870     PRINT "TRY AGAIN.": GOTO 830
880     DIM N$(NU): FOR I = 1 TO NU
890     PRINT "VARIABLE X";I;: INPUT " REPRESENTS ";N$(I)
900     NEXT I
910     PRINT
920     PRINT "REMEMBER ONLY EQUATIONS WITH"
930     PRINT "DECISION VARIABLES COUNT IN"
940     PRINT "ANSWERING NEXT QUESTION."
950     INPUT "NUMBER OF CONSTRAINTS ";MC
960     PRINT
970     INPUT "NO. OF DEVIATIONAL VARIABLES? ";DV
980     PRINT
990     INPUT "NUMBER OF PRIORITIES ";P
1000    PRINT
1010    DIM A(DV,NU + (2 * DV) + 1)
1020    DIM CZ(P,NU + 2 * DV +1)
1030    DIM C(NU + 2 * DV)
1040    DIM B(DV)
1050    DIM WC(NU + (2 * DV))
1060    DIM WB(DV)
1070    DIM Y$(DV),DI(NU + 2 * DV)
1080    FOR I = 1 TO MC
1090    HOME : PRINT "IF ONLY 3 OR 4 UNKNOWNS IN PROBLEM"
1100    PRINT "ANSWER NEXT QUESTION WITH 'A'."
1110    PRINT "IT WILL BE FASTER TO ENTER ALL."
1120    PRINT : PRINT "TYPE IN NUMBER OF VARIABLES"
1130    PRINT "WHICH APPEAR IN EQUATION ";I
1140    INPUT "OR A FOR (A)LL. ";AA$
1150    IF AA$ = "A" THEN GOTO 1240
1160  AA = VAL (AA$)
1170    FOR J = 1 TO AA
1180    PRINT "ENTER SUBSCRIPT OF UNKNOWN ";J
1190    PRINT "IN EQUATION ";I;" ";: INPUT BB$
```

```
1200    PRINT "ENTER VALUE OF X";BB$;" ";: INPUT A$
1210   A(I, VAL (BB$)) = VAL (A$)
1220    NEXT J
1230    GOTO 1280
1240    FOR J = 1 TO NU
1250    PRINT "ENTER VALUE OF X";J;" ";: INPUT A$
1260   A(I,J) = VAL (A$)
1270    NEXT J
1280    PRINT
1290    PRINT "IS POS. DEV. VAR. ALLOWED IN"
1300    PRINT "EQUATION ";I; " ";: INPUT CC$
1310    IF CC$ = "N" THEN GOTO 1350
1320    IF CC$ = "Y" THEN GOTO 1340
1330    PRINT "Y OR N ONLY. TRY AGAIN.": GOTO 1280
1340   A(I,NU + I) = 1:A(I,NU + DV + I) = - 1: GOTO 1360
1350   A(I,NU + I) = 1
1360    PRINT "RHS FOR EQUATION ";I;" ";: INPUT A$
1370   A(I,NU + 2 * DV + 1) = VAL (A$)
1380    IF A(I,NU + 2 * DV + 1) > = 0 THEN GOTO 1420
1390    FOR J = 1 TO NU + 2 * DV + 1
1400   A(I,J) = A(I,J) * - 1
1410    NEXT J
1420    PRINT
1430    PRINT "EQUATION ";I;" READS:"
1440    PRINT
1450    FOR J = 1 TO NU
1460    PRINT A(I,J);"X";J;" + ";
1470    NEXT J
1480    PRINT "D";I;"—";
1490    IF CC$ = "Y" THEN PRINT " — D";I;"+";
1500    PRINT " = ";
1510    PRINT A(I,NU + 2 * MC + 1)
1520    PRINT "IS IT RIGHT?";: INPUT A$
1530    IF A$ = "Y" THEN GOTO 1560
1540    IF A$ = "N" THEN HOME: PRINT "REENTER EQUATION ";I;".":
           GOTO 1170
1550    PRINT "Y OR N ONLY. TRY AGAIN.": GOTO 1520
1560    NEXT I
1570    IF DV > MC THEN PRINT "YOUR DEV. VARS. NOT IN OTHER
           CONSTRAINTS ARE:": GO TO 1590
1580    GOTO 1840
1590    PRINT "D";MC + 1;" TO D";DV
1600    FOR I = MC + 1 TO DV
1610    PRINT
1620    PRINT "HOW MANY OTHER DEV. VARS. APPEAR"
1630    PRINT "IN EQUATION FOR D";I;: INPUT SS
1640    IF SS = 0 THEN NEXT I
1650    FOR J = 1 TO SS
```

```
1660    PRINT "EQUATION NUMBER OF DEV. VAR. ";J;" IN D";I;:
        INPUT TT
1670    INPUT "(P)OS OR (N)EG DEV. VAR.? ";VV$
1680    IF VV$ = "P" THEN GOTO 1690
1681    IF VV$ = "N" THEN GOTO 1690
1682    GOTO 1670
1690    INPUT "(P)OS OR (N)EG VALUE? ";WW$
1700    IF WW$ = "P" THEN GOTO 1710
1701    IF WW$ = "N" THEN GOTO 1710
1702    GOTO 1690
1710    IF VV$ = "P" AND WW$ = "P" THEN A(I,NU + DV + TT) = 1
1720    IF VV$ = "P" AND WW$ = "N" THEN A(I,NU + DV + TT) =
        - 1
1730    IF VV$ = "N" AND WW$ = "P" THEN A(I,NU + TT) = 1
1740    IF VV$ = "N" AND WW$ = "N" THEN A(I,NU + TT) = - 1
1750  A(I,NU + I) = 1:A(I,NU + DV + I) = - 1
1760    NEXT J
1770    PRINT "RHS FOR THIS EQUATION? ";: INPUT A(I,NU + 2 *
        DV + 1)
1780    IF A(I,NU + 2 * DV + 1) > = 0 THEN GOTO 1820
1790    FOR J = 1 TO NU + 2 * MC + 1
1800  A(I,J) = A(I,J) * - 1
1810    NEXT J
1820    NEXT I
1830  MC = DV
1840  L = 1
1850    PRINT
1860    FOR J = NU + 1 TO NU + MC
1870    PRINT "PRIORITY ASSOCIATED WITH D";L;" - ";: INPUT A$
1880    IF A$ = CHR$ (13) THEN C(J) = 0: GOTO 1900
1890  C(J) = VAL (A$)
1900    INPUT "WEIGHT FOR THE DEV.VAR.";A$
1910    IF A$ = CHR$ (13) THEN WC(J) = 0: GOTO 1930
1920  WC(J) = VAL (A$)
1930  L = L + 1
1940    NEXT J
1950  L = 1
1960    FOR J = NU + MC + 1 TO NU + (2 * MC)
1970    PRINT "PRIORITY ASSOCIATED WITH D";L;" + ";: INPUT A$
1980    IF A$ = CHR$ (13) THEN C(J) = 0: GOTO 2000
1990  C(J) = VAL (A$)
2000    INPUT "WEIGHT FOR THE DEV.VAR.";A$
2010    IF A$ = CHR$ (13) THEN WC(J) = 0: GOTO 2030
2020  WC(J) = VAL (A$)
2030  L = L + 1
2040    PRINT
2050    NEXT J
2060    RETURN
```

```
2070    REM   CB IN INITIAL TABLEAU
2080    I = 1
2090    FOR J = NU + 1 TO NU + MC
2100    B(I) = C(J)
2110    WB(I) = WC(J):Y$(I) = "D" + STR$ (J - NU) + "-"
2120    I = I + 1
2130    NEXT J
2140    RETURN
2150    REM   INSTRUCTIONS
2160    HOME
2170    PRINT "THIS PROBLEM SOLVES A GOAL PROGRAMMING"
2180    PRINT "PROBLEM BUT NEEDS A LITTLE INTRO."
2190    PRINT
2200    PRINT "TO THIS END, 'SCHNIEDERJANS'"
2210    PRINT "EXAMPLE' HAS BEEN PROVIDED"
2220    PRINT "ON DISKETTE. IT IS PRETTY STRAIGHT— "
2230    PRINT "FORWARD EXCEPT FOR THE"
2240    PRINT "PRIORITIES WHERE, FOR MODELING"
2250    PRINT "REASONS, THE ARTIFICIAL, OR 0,"
2260    PRINT "PRIORITY BECOMES PRIORITY 1 AND"
2270    PRINT "ALL THE OTHER, STATED, PRIORITIES"
2280    PRINT "SLIP DOWN ONE. INSTEAD OF 'FOUR'"
2290    PRINT "THE ANSWER TO THE QUESTION, 'NUMBER"
2230    PRINT "OF PRIORITIES?' IS 'FIVE'."
2310    PRINT "THE OPERATOR MUST MAKE THIS"
2320    PRINT "CONVERSION."
2330    PRINT: PRINT "PRESS ANY KEY TO CONTINUE.";: GET Q$
2340    HOME
2350    PRINT "ANOTHER PROGRAM QUIRK OCCURS IF THERE"
2360    PRINT "ARE NO UNKNOWNS (JUST DEV. VARS.)
2365    PRINT "IN AN EQUATION."
2370    PRINT "WHEN IT ASKS FOR NUMBER OF CONSTRAINTS"
2380    PRINT "ONLY ENTER THE NUMBER IN WHICH"
2390    PRINT "UNKNOWNS APPEAR."
2400    PRINT "DON'T TRY TO SUBSTITUTE DEVIATIONAL"
2410    PRINT "VARIABLES INTO CONSTRAINTS LIKE"
2420    PRINT "YOU MIGHT TRY TO DO TO LIMIT OVERTIME."
2430    PRINT "INSTEAD, PROGRAM WILL CREATE"
2440    PRINT "SEPARATE EQUATIONS FOR STAND ALONE"
2450    PRINT "DEVIATIONAL VARIABLES AS YOU"
2460    PRINT "ANSWER FURTHER QUESTIONS ABOUT"
2470    PRINT "DEV. VARS. IN EXCESS OF CONSTRAINTS."
2480    PRINT: PRINT "PRESS ANY KEY TO CONTINUE.";: GET Q$
2490    HOME
2660    PRINT "TABLEAUX ARE NOT NEAT. THEY"
2670    PRINT "ARE JAMMED TOGETHER IN THE ATTEMPT"
2680    PRINT "TO GET ALL ON THE FEWEST PRINTER"
2690    PRINT "LINES. THE OPTION TO PRINT"
```

```
2700      PRINT "THEM IS PROVIDED FOR CHECKOUT"
2710      PRINT "PURPOSES ONLY. READ STARTING WITH"
2720      PRINT "RHS COLUMN ON LEFT IN A(I,J) PORTION"
2730      PRINT "AND AMOUNT OF REMAINING PRIORITY"
2740      PRINT "TO FILL ON LEFT IN ZJ-CZ PORTION."
2750      PRINT
2760      PRINT "CB AND CJ ARE NOT PRINTED."
2770      PRINT "YOU CAN DETERMINE WHAT THEY ARE AT"
2780      PRINT "END OF RUN BY ASKING FOR PRINT"
2790      PRINT "OF 'C(I)' AND 'WC(I)' FOR CJ"
2800      PRINT "WHERE 'I' IS COLUMN NUMBER, 'C(I)'"
2810      PRINT "IS THE SUBSCRIPT PRIORITY AND 'WC(I)'"
2820      PRINT "IS THE WEIGHT ASSIGNED."
2830      PRINT "THE SAME IS TRUE FOR 'CB' USING"
2840      PRINT "'B(I)' AND 'WB(I)'
2850      PRINT "WHERE 'I' IS THE ROW NUMBER."
2860      PRINT "PRESS ANY KEY TO CONTINUE. ';: GET Q$
2870      HOME
2880      PRINT "THE OTHER IMPORTANT VARIABLE NAMES"
2890      PRINT "ARE 'A(I,J)' FOR A(I,J)"
2900      PRINT "AND 'CZ(I,J)' FOR ZJ-CJ"
2910      PRINT "WHERE 'I' IS 1 TO NUMBER OF DEV."
2920      PRINT "VARS. IN A(I,J) AND 1 TO NUMBER"
2930      PRINT "OF PRIORITIES IN CZ(I,J) AND"
2940      PRINT "J IS 1 TO NUMBER OF CONSTRAINTS PLUS"
2950      PRINT "TWICE THE NUMBER OF DEV. VARS. PLUS"
2960      PRINT "ONE(TO INCLUDE RHS) IN BOTH CASES."
2970      PRINT
2980      PRINT "PRESS ANY KEY TO CONTINUE.";: GET Q$
2990      HOME
3000      PRINT "TO RUN PROGRAM, THE FIRST QUESTION"
3010      PRINT "GOT YOU HERE. THE NEXT WILL"
3020      PRINT "ASK WHETHER OR NOT YOUR PROBLEM"
3030      PRINT "IS ALREADY ON FILE (THE DISK)."
3040      PRINT "ANSWER 'Y' OR 'N' AS APPROPRIATE."
3050      PRINT "THE NEXT QUESTION ASKS YOU TO"
3060      PRINT "NAME YOUR PROBLEM."
3070      PRINT "BE CAREFUL NOT TO USE A NAME"
3080      PRINT "OF A FILE ALREADY ON DISK."
3090      PRINT: FLASH : PRINT "IT WILL GET WIPED OUT.": NORMAL
3100      PRINT: PRINT "TO CHANGE A PROBLEM ON DISK ANSWER
             YES"
3110      PRINT "TO NEXT QUESTION.  TO RERUN A PROBLEM"
3120      PRINT "ALREADY ON DISK ANSWER NO TO"
3130      PRINT "THIS QUESTION AND PROGRAM WILL"
3140      PRINT "MERELY REGURGITATE A PREVIOUSLY"
3150      PRINT "STORED PROBLEM AFTER YOU ANSWER"
3160      PRINT "THE FINAL QUESTION ON PRINTING."
```

```
3170      PRINT : PRINT "I THINK THAT SHOULD BE ENOUGH"
3180      PRINT "TO ALLOW YOU TO RUN PROGRAM."
3190      PRINT : PRINT "PRESS ANY KEY TO START";: GET Q$
3200      HOME : RETURN
3210      REM    CHECK FOR DONE
3220   Z = 0
3230      FOR K = 1 TO P
3240      IF CZ(K,NU + 2 * MC + 1) > 0 THEN GOTO 3270
3250      NEXT K
3260      GOTO 5230
3270      IF K > 1 AND Z = 0 THEN GOTO 3550
3280      IF K > 1 THEN GOTO 3380
3290      FOR J = 1 TO NU + 2 * MC
3300      IF CZ(K,J) > 0 AND J < NU + 1 THEN RETURN
3310      IF CZ(K,J) > 0 AND K < C(J) THEN RETURN
3320      NEXT J
3330      NEXT K
3340      PRINT "NO POS VALUES IN PRIORITY 1."
3350      PRINT "PROBLEM IS INFEASIBLE."
3360      PRINT "PRESENT STATUS IS:
3370      PRINT : GOTO 5230
3380      FOR J = 1 TO NU + 2 * MC
3390      IF CZ(K,J) > 0 THEN GOTO 3430
3400      NEXT J
3410      NEXT K
3420      GOTO 5230
3430      FOR M = 1 TO K − 1
3440      IF CZ(M,J) < 0 THEN GOTO 3470
3450      NEXT M
3460      GOTO 3500
3470      NEXT J
3480      NEXT K
3490      GOTO 5230
3500      IF J < NU + 1 THEN RETURN
3510      IF K < C(J) THEN RETURN
3520      NEXT J
3530      NEXT K
3540      GOTO 5230
3550   Z = Z + 1
3560      FOR I = 1 TO K − 1
3570      IF CZ(I,NU + 2 * MC + 1) = 0 THEN GOTO 3590
3580      NEXT I
3590      FOR J = 1 TO NU + 2 * MC
3600      IF CZ(I,J) > 0 THEN GOTO 3640
3610      NEXT J
3620      NEXT I
3630      GOTO 3380
3640      IF I = 1 THEN RETURN
```

```
3650    FOR L = 1 TO M − 1
3660    IF CZ(L,J) < 0 THEN GOTO 3610
3670    NEXT L
3680    IF J < NU + 1 THEN RETURN
3690    IF I < C(J) THEN RETURN
3700    GOTO 3610
3710    REM    DETERMINE PIVOT COLUMN
3720  Z = 0:I = 0
3730    FOR K = 1 TO P
3740    FOR J = 1 TO NU + 2 * MC
3750    IF CZ(K,J) < = 0 THEN GOTO 3820
3760    IF CZ(K,J) < Z THEN GOTO 3820
3770    IF CZ(K,J) = > Z THEN GOSUB 3830
3780    IF CV = 1 THEN CV = 0: GOTO 3820
3790    IF CZ(K,J) = 0 THEN GOTO 3810
3800    IF CZ(K,J) > Z THEN Z = CZ(K,J):I = 1:DI(1) = J: GOTO
            3820
3810  I = I + 1:DI(I) = J
3820    NEXT J: GOTO 3920
3830  CV = 0
3840    IF K = 1 THEN RETURN
3850    IF K = 2 THEN GOTO 3900
3860    FOR JJ = K − 1 TO 1 STEP − 1
3870    IF CZ(JJ,J) < 0 THEN CV = 1: RETURN
3880    NEXT JJ
3890    RETURN
3900    IF CZ(1,J) < 0 THEN CV = 1
3910    RETURN
3920    IF I = 1 THEN M = DI(1):TB = K: GOTO 4300
3930    IF I > 1 THEN GOTO 3950
3940    NEXT K: GOTO 5230
3950  Z = 0:II = 0
3960    IF K > = P THEN GOSUB 4310
3970  M = DI(1 + QZ):TB = P
3980    FOR L = K + 1 TO P
3990    FOR J = 1 TO I
4000    IF CZ(L,DI(J)) < = 0 THEN GOTO 4070
4010    IF CZ(L,DI(J)) < Z THEN GOTO 4070
4020    IF CZ(L,DI(J)) > = Z THEN GOSUB 4080
4030    IF CV = 1 THEN CV = 0: GOTO 4070
4040    IF CZ(L,DI(J)) = Z THEN GOTO 4060
4050    IF CZ(L,DI(J)) > Z THEN Z = CZ(L,DI(J)):II = 1:DB(II) = DI(J):
            GOTO 4070
4060  II = II + 1:DB(II) = DI(J)
4070    NEXT J: GOTO 4160
4080  CV = 0
4090    IF L = 2 THEN GOTO 4140
4100    FOR JJ = L − 1 TO L STEP − 1
```

```
4110    IF CZ(JJ,DI(J)) < 0 THEN CV = 1: RETURN
4120    NEXT JJ
4130    RETURN
4140    IF CZ(1,DI(J)) < 0 THEN CV = 1
4150    RETURN
4160    IF II > 0 THEN I = II
4170    IF Z = 0 THEN GOTO 4270
4180    IF II = 1 THEN M = DB(1):TB = L: GOTO 4300
4190    IF L > = P AND II = 0 THEN GOSUB 4310
4200  M = DI(QZ + 1):TB = P: RETURN
4210    IF L > = P THEN GOSUB 4330
4220  M = DB(1 + QZ):TB = P: RETURN
4230    FOR J = 1 TO II
4240  DI(J) = DB(J)
4250    NEXT J
4260  Z = 0:II = 0
4270    NEXT L
4280    GOSUB 4310
4290  M = DI(1):TB = 1: RETURN
4300    RETURN
4310    IF I = QZ THEN PRINT "ALL PIVOTS TRIED": PRINT "NO
        WAY OUT OF LOOP": PRINT "CURRENT STATUS IS:":
        GOTO 5230
4320    RETURN
4330    IF II = QZ THEN PRINT "ALL PIVOTS TRIED": PRINT "NO
        WAY OUT OF LOOP": PRINT "CURRENT STATUS IS:":
        GOTO 5230
4340    RETURN
4350    REM    DETERMINE PIVOT ROW
4360  P2 = P1:P1 = PC:PC = M:M = 1
4370    IF QQ$ = "F" AND TC > 0 THEN GOTO 4390
4380    IF TB$ = "Y" THEN PRINT D$"PR#1"
4390    PRINT "PIVOT COLUMN = ";PC
4400    IF TB$ = "Y" THEN PRINT D$"PR#0"
4410  J = 0:M = 0:DR = 0
4420    FOR I = 1 TO MC
4430    IF A(I,PC) < = 0 THEN DI(I) = 0: GOTO 4500
4440  DI(I) = A(I,(NU + 2 * MC + 1)) / A(I,PC)
4450    IF DI(I) < 0 THEN GOTO 4500
4460    IF DR = 0 THEN GOTO 4480
4470    IF DI(I) > DR THEN GOTO 4500
4480    IF DI(I) < DR OR DR = 0 THEN M = I:DR = DI(I):J = 1:DB(J)
        = I: GOTO 4500
4490    IF DI(I) = DR AND DR > 0 THEN J = J + 1:DB(J) = I
4500    NEXT I
4510    IF J = 0 THEN PRINT "THE SOLUTION IS UNBOUNDED.":
        END
4520    IF J = 1 THEN GOTO 4680
```

```
4530   DR = O:K = 0
4540    FOR I = 1 TO J
4550    IF B(DB(I)) < 0 THEN GOTO 4600
4560    IF DR = 0 THEN GOTO 4580
4570    IF B(DB(I)) > DR THEN GOTO 4600
4580    IF B(DB(I)) < DR OR DR = 0 THEN M = DB(I):DR =
           B(DB(I)):K = 1:DI(K) = DB(I): GOTO 4600
4590    IF B(DB(I)) = DR AND DR > 0 THEN K = K + 1:DI(K) =
           DB(I)
4600    NEXT I
4610    IF K = 0 OR K = 1 THEN GOTO 4680
4620   DR = 0:L = 0
4630    FOR I = 1 TO K
4640    IF WB(DI(I)) < DR THEN GOTO 4670
4650    IF WB(DI(I)) > DR THEN M = DI(I):DR = WB(DI(I)):L =
           1:DB(L) = DI(I): GOTO 4670
4660    IF WB(DI(I)) = DR THEN L = L + 1:DB(L) = DI(I)
4670    NEXT I
4680    RETURN
4690    REM   DETERMINE COEFFICIENTS FOR NEXT TABLEAU
4700    IF QQ$ = "F" AND TC > 0 THEN GOTO 4720
4710    IF TB$ = "Y" THEN PRINT D$PR#1"
4720   P4 = P3:P3 = PR:PR = M:M = 1:DI = A(PR,PC)
4730    PRINT "PIVOT ROW = ";PR: PRINT
4740    IF TB$ = "Y" THEN PRINT D$"PR#0"
4750    IF PC = P2 AND PR = P4 THEN PRINT "IN A LOOP, TRYING
           AGAIN.": GOTO 4960
4760   QZ = 0
4770    FOR J = 1 TO NU + (2 * MC) + 1
4780   A(PR,J) = A(PR,J) / DI
4790    NEXT J
4800    FOR I = 1 TO MC: GOTO 4810
4810    IF I = PR THEN NEXT I: GOTO 4870
4820   DI = A(I,PC)
4830    FOR J = 1 TO NU + (2 * MC) + 1
4840   A(I,J) = A(I,J) - (DI * A(PR,J))
4850    NEXT J
4860    NEXT I
4870   B(PR) = C(PC)
4880   WB(PR) = WC(PC)
4890   TC = TC + 1
4900    IF PC < = NU THEN Y$(PR) = "X" + STR$ (PC): RETURN
4910    IF PC > NU AND PC < NU + MC + 1 THEN Y$(PR) = "D" +
           STR$ (PC - NU) + "-" :RETURN
4920   Y$(PR) = "D" + STR$ (PC - NU - MC) + "+"
4930    RETURN
4940    REM   LAST THREE ROWS BROUGHT NEW VARIABLE
           NAMES
```

```
4950      REM   AND WEIGHTS/PRIORITIES INTO BASIS
4960   QZ = QZ + 1
4970      FOR J = 1 TO NU + 2 * MC
4980      IF J = PC THEN GOTO 5000
4990      IF CZ(TB,J) = CZ(TB,PC) THEN GOTO 430
5000      NEXT J
5010      GOTO 5230
5020      REM    TABLEAU PRINTOUT
5030      IF TB$ = "Y" THEN PRINT D$"PR#1"
5040      PRINT
5050      PRINT "COEFFICIENTS IN TABLEAU:"
5060      PRINT
5070      FOR I = 1 TO MC
5080      PRINT Y$(I);" ";A(I,NU + (2 * MC) + 1);" ";
5090      FOR J = 1 TO NU + (2 * MC)
5100      PRINT A(I,J);" ";
5110      NEXT J: PRINT : NEXT I
5120      PRINT
5130      PRINT "VALUES IN ZJ-CJ:"
5140      PRINT
5150      FOR K = P TO 1 STEP − 1
5160      PRINT "P";K;" ";
5170      PRINT CZ(K,NU + (2 * MC) + 1);" ";
5180      FOR J = 1 TO NU + (2 * MC)
5190      PRINT CZ(K,J);" ";
5200      NEXT J: PRINT : NEXT K
5210      IF TB$ = "Y" THEN PRINT D$"PR#0"
5220      RETURN
5230      REM   SOLUTION PRINTOUT
5240      IF PO$ = "Y" THEN PRINT D$"PR#1"
5250      PRINT
5260      PRINT "SOLUTION VARIABLES ARE:"
5270      PRINT
5280      FOR I = 1 TO MC
5290   QQ = LEN (Y$(I))
5300      IF N$ = "Y" AND LEFT$ (Y$(I),1) = "X" THEN PP$ = RIGHT$
          (Y$(I),QQ − 1):PP = VAL (PP$): PRINT N$(PP);: HTAB 20:
          PRINT A(I,NU + (2 * MC) + 1): GOTO 5320
5310      PRINT Y$(I);: HTAB 20: PRINT A(I,NU + (2 * MC) + 1): GOTO
          5320
5320      NEXT I
5330      PRINT
5340   Z = 0
5350      PRINT "UNACHIEVED GOALS ARE:"
5360      PRINT
5370      FOR K = 1 TO P
5380      IF CZ(K,NU + (2 * MC) + 1) = 0 THEN GOTO 5400
5390      PRINT "P";K;: HTAB 20: PRINT CZ(K,NU + (2 * MC) + 1):Z =
          1
```

```
5400      NEXT K
5410      IF Z = 0 THEN PRINT "NONE": PRINT : PRINT: PRINT
5420      IF PO$ = "Y" THEN PRINT D$"PR#0"
5430      PRINT "PRESS 'R' TO DO ANOTHER PROBLEM"
5440      INPUT "OR PRESS 'Q' TO QUIT.";X$
5450      IF X$ = "Q" THEN END
5460      IF X$ = "R" THEN HOME: GOTO 10
5470      PRINT "YOU HIT A WRONG KEY.": GOTO 5430
5480      REM    ZJ CALCULATION
5490   Z = 0
5500      FOR K = 1 TO P
5510      FOR J = 1 TO NU + (2 * MC) + 1
5520      FOR I = 1 TO MC
5530      IF B(I) = K THEN Z = Z + WB(I) * A(I,J)
5540      NEXT I
5550   CZ(K,J) = Z
5560   Z = 0
5570      IF J = NU + 2 * MC + 1 THEN GOTO 5590
5580      IF C(J) = K THEN CZ(K,J) = CZ(K,J) = WC(J)
5590      NEXT J
5600      NEXT K
5610      RETURN
5620      REM    PRIORITY AND WEIGHT PRINTOUT
5630      IF TB$ = "Y" THEN PRINT D$"PR#1"
5640      IF TB$ = "N" THEN RETURN
5650      IF QQ$ = "F" AND TC > 0 THEN RETURN
5660      IF TC = 0 THEN I = 1:K = 1: PRINT : GOTO 5680
5670      RETURN
5680      FOR J = NU + 1 TO NU + MC: PRINT "D";I;" - ";C(J);: HTAB
            30: PRINT "WT ";WC(J)
5690   I = I + 1: NEXT J
5700      FOR J = NU + MC + 1 TO NU + (2 * MC): PRINT "D";K;" +
            ";C(J);: HTAB 30: PRINT "WT ";WC(J)
5710   K = K + 1: NEXT J
5720      IF TB$ = "Y" THEN PRINT D$"PR#0"
5730      RETURN
5740      REM    WRITE SUBROUTINE
5750      PRINT D$"OPEN";PR$;",L300"
5760      FOR I = 1 TO MC
5770      PRINT D$"WRITE";PR$;",R";I
5780      FOR J = 1 TO NU + (MC * 2) + 1
5790      PRINT A(I,J)
5800      NEXT J
5810      NEXT I
5820   I = MC + 1
5830      PRINT D$"WRITE";PR$;",R";I
5840      FOR J = 1 TO NU + (2 * MC)
5850      PRINT C(J)
5860      NEXT J
```

```
5870    I = I + 1
5880    PRINT D$"WRITE";PR$;",R";I
5890    FOR J = 1 TO NU + (2 * MC)
5900    PRINT WC(J)
5910    NEXT J
5920    I = I + 1
5930    IF N$ = "Y" THEN PRINT D$"WRITE";PR$;",R";I: GOTO 5950
5940    GOTO 5980
5950    FOR J = 1 TO NU
5960    PRINT N$(J)
5970    NEXT J
5980    PRINT D$"WRITE";PR$;",R";0
5990    PRINT NU: PRINT MC: PRINT P: PRINT N$
6000    PRINT D$"CLOSE";PR$;" "
6010    RETURN
6020    REM   CHANGE SUBROUTINE
6030    HOME : PRINT
6040    PRINT "IF YOU WANT TO CHANGE PRIORITIES"
6050    PRINT "ANSWER TO EQUATION NO. IS ";MC + 1
6060    PRINT "IF YOU WANT TO CHANGE WEIGHTS"
6070    PRINT "ANSWER TO EQUATION NO. IS ";MC + 2
6080    PRINT "IF YOU WANT TO ADD OR DELETE"
6090    PRINT "PRIORITIES OR CONSTRAINTS"
6100    PRINT "RESET AND RUN A NEW PROBLEM."
6110    PRINT
6120    PRINT "ANSWER QUESTIONS ABOUT WHAT"
6130    PRINT "UNKNOWN OR DEV. VAR. WITH THE "
6140    PRINT "FULL NAME (E.G. 'X1' OR 'D1 +')."
6150    PRINT
6160    INPUT "WHAT EQUATION NUMBER? ";KK
6170    IF KK > MC + 2 THEN PRINT "NOT THAT MANY
           EQUATIONS. ONLY ";MC: GOTO 6190
6180    GOTO 6200
6190    PRINT "PLUS 2 FOR WEIGHTS AND PRIORITIES.": GOTO
           6160
6200    PRINT
6210    IF KK = MC + 1 THEN GOTO 6530
6220    IF KK = MC + 2 THEN GOTO 6720
6230    IF KK < = MC THEN PRINT "IF YOU WANT TO CHANGE
           RHS,"
6240    PRINT "THE ANSWER TO 'WHAT VARIABLE' IS"
6250    PRINT "'RHS'."
6260    PRINT
6270    INPUT "WHAT VARIABLE? "?JJ$
6280    PRINT "WHAT IS NEW VALUE OF ";JJ$;: INPUT JJ: PRINT
6290    IF JJ$ = "RHS" THEN A(KK,NU + 2 * MC + 1) = JJ: GOTO
           6910
6300    IF LEFT$ (JJ$,1) = "X" THEN GOTO 6350
```

```
6310    IF LEFT$ (JJ$,1) = "D" AND RIGHT$ (JJ$,1) = "+" THEN
          GOTO 6410
6320    IF LEFT$ (JJ$,1) = "D" AND RIGHT$ (JJ$,1) = "−" THEN
          GOTO 6470
6330    PRINT "DIDN'T ANSWER WITH XI, DI+, DI− OR"
6340    PRINT "RHS. TRY AGAIN.": GOTO 6270
6350    IF LEN (JJ$) = 2 THEN JJ$ = RIGHT$ (JJ$,1)
6360    IF LEN (JJ$) = 3 THEN JJ$ = RIGHT$ (JJ$,2)
6370    J = VAL (JJ$)
6380    IF J > NU THEN PRINT "NO SUCH VARIABLE. TRY AGAIN.":
          GOTO 6270
6390    A(KK,J) = JJ
6400      GOTO 6910
6410    IF LEN (JJ$) = 4 THEN JJ$ = MID$ (JJ$2,2)
6420    IF LEN (JJ$) = 3 THEN JJ$ = MID$ (JJ$,2,1)
6430    J = VAL (JJ$)
6440    IF J > MC THEN PRINT "NO SUCH DEV. VAR. TRY AGAIN.":
          GOTO 6270
6450    A(KK,J + NU + MC) = JJ
6460      GOTO 6910
6470    IF LEN (JJ$) = 4 THEN JJ$ = MID$ (JJ$,2,2)
6480    IF LEN (JJ$) = 3 THEN JJ$ = MID$ (JJ$2,1)
6490    J = VAL (JJ$)
6500    IF J > MC THEN PRINT "NO SUCH DEV.VAR. TRY AGAIN.":
          GOTO 6270
6510    A(KK,J + NU) + JJ
6520      GOTO 6910
6530    INPUT "WHAT DEV. VAR.'S PRIORITY? ";JJ$
6540    PRINT "WHAT IS NEW PRIORITY FOR "JJ$";: INPUT JJ
6550    IF LEFT$ (JJ$,1) < > "D" THEN PRINT "NEED A D TO
          PROCESS.": GOTO 6530
6560    IF RIGHT$ (JJ$,1) = "+" THEN GOTO 6580
6570    IF RIGHT$ (JJ$,1) = "−" THEN GOTO 6630
6580    IF LEN (JJ$) = 4 THEN JJ$ = MID$ (JJ HGR ,2,2)
6590  . IF LEN (JJ$) = 3 THEN JJ$ = MID$ (JJ$,2,1)
6600    J = VAL (JJ$)
6610    C(J + NU + MC) = JJ
6620      GOTO 6670
6630    IF LEN (JJ$) = 4 THEN JJ$ = MID$ (JJ$,2,2)
6640    IF LEN (JJ$) = 3 THEN JJ$ = MID$ (JJ$,2,1)
6650    J = VAL (JJ$)
6660    C(J + NU) = JJ
6670      PRINT
6680    INPUT "ANOTHER PRIORITY? ";Q$
6690    IF Q$ = "Y" THEN GOTO 6530
6700    IF Q$ = "N" THEN GOTO 7030
6710    PRINT "Y OR N ONLY. TRY AGAIN.": GOTO 6680
6720    INPUT "WHAT DEV. VAR.'S WEIGHT? ";JJ$
```

```
6730      PRINT "WHAT IS NEW WEIGHT FOR ";JJ$;: INPUT JJ
6740      IF LEFT$ (JJ$,1) < > "D" THEN GOTO 6770
6750      IF RIGHT$ (JJ$,1) = "+" THEN GOTO 6770
6760      IF RIGHT$ (JJ$,1) = "−" THEN GOTO 6820
6770      IF LEN (JJ$) = 4 THEN JJ$ = MID$ (JJ$,2,2)
6780      IF LEN (JJ$) = 3 THEN JJ$ = MID$ (JJ$,2,1)
6790   J = VAL (JJ$)
6800   WC(J + NU + MC) = JJ
6810      GOTO 6860
6820      IF LEN (JJ$) = 4 THEN JJ$ = MID$ (JJ$,2,2)
6830      IF LEN (JJ$) = 3 THEN JJ$ = MID$ (JJ$,2,1)
6840   J = VAL (JJ$)
6850   WC(J + NU) = JJ
6860      PRINT
6870      INPUT "ANOTHER WEIGHT? ";Q$
6880      IF Q$ = "Y" THEN GOTO 6720
6890      IF Q$ = "N" THEN GOTO 7100
6900      PRINT "Y OR N ONLY. TRY AGAIN.": GOTO 6870
6910      PRINT
6920      INPUT "ANOTHER VALUE, SAME EQUATION? ";Q$
6930      IF Q$ = "Y" THEN GOTO 6270
6940      IF Q$ = "N" THEN GOTO 6960
6950      PRINT "Y OR N ONLY. TRY AGAIN.": GOTO 6920
6960      PRINT D$"OPEN";PR$;",L300"
6970      PRINT D$"WRITE";PR$;",R";KK
6980      FOR I = 1 TO NU + 2 * MC + 1
6990      PRINT A(KK,I)
7000      NEXT I
7010      PRINT D$"CLOSE";PR$
7020      GOTO 7160
7030      PRINT D$"OPEN";PR$;",L300"
7040      PRINT D$"WRITE";PR$;",R";KK
7050      FOR I = 1 TO NU + 2 * MC
7060      PRINT C(I)
7070      NEXT I
7080      PRINT D$"CLOSE";PR$
7090      GOTO 7160
7100      PRINT D$"OPEN";PR$;",L300"
7110      PRINT D$"WRITE";PR$;",R";KK
7120      FOR I = 1 TO NU + 2 * MC
7130      PRINT WC(I)
7140      NEXT I
7150      PRINT D$"CLOSE";PR$
7160      PRINT
7170      INPUT "ANY MORE CHANGES?";Q$
7180      IF Q$ = "Y" THEN GOTO 6160
7190      IF Q$ = "N" THEN RETURN
7200      PRINT "Y OR N ONLY. TRY AGAIN": GOTO 7170
```

Index